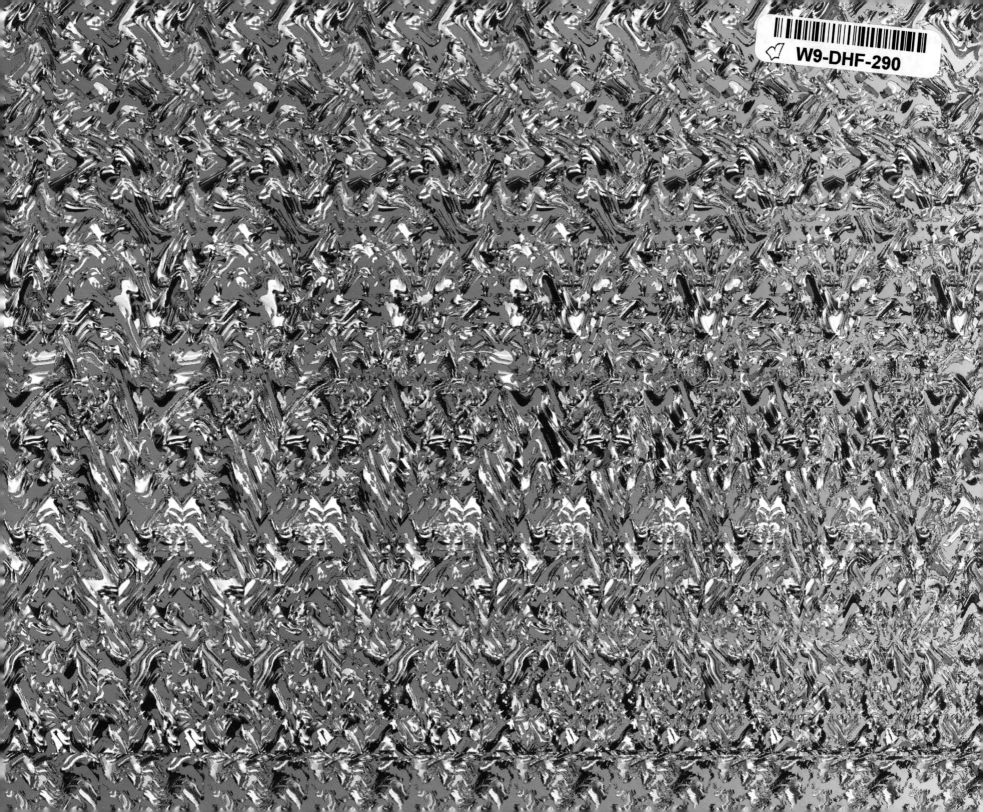

MAGIC EYE®

Amazing 3D Illusions
by Magic Eye Inc.

Andrews McMeel
Publishing

Kansas City

The material in this volume originally appeared in *Magic Eye: A New Way of Looking at the World, Magic Eye II: Now You See It...* , and *Magic Eye III—Visions: A New Dimension in Art.*

ISBN: 0-7407-4065-2
"Children" photo, page 10, © Melanie Carr, Courtesy of Southern Stock Uniphoto Press International.

This edition was produced exclusively for Barnes & Noble, Inc., by Andrews McMeel Publishing.

ATTENTION: SCHOOLS AND BUSINESSES

Magic Eye® Images are available for educational, business, or sales promotional use. For information, contact:

Magic Eye Inc., PO Box 1986, Provincetown, MA 02657
www.magiceye.com

Andrews & McMeel books are available at quantity discounts with bulk purchase for educational, business, or sales promotional use. For information, please write to: Special Sales Department, Andrews McMeel Publishing, 4520 Main Street, Kansas City, Mo 64111.

INTRODUCTION

Magic Eye®3D Illusions are amazing and will challenge and entertain you. Embedded within each Magic Eye image is an enchanting 3D hidden object that materializes before your eyes!

How did we invent this amazing illusion? The basic concept has been around for many years. In 1959, Dr. Bella Julesz was the first to use two computer-generated 3D images made up of randomly placed dots to study depth perception in human beings. The two images were viewed side by side. Because the dot pictures did not contain any other information, like color or shapes, he could be sure that when his subject saw the picture, it was 3D only.

In 1979, Christopher Tyler, a student of Dr. Julesz, discovered that the offset scheme could be applied to a single image. This was the birth of the black-and-white single-image random dot stereogram.

In 1991, Programmer Tom Baccei and Artist Cheri Smith collaborated to create 3D art based on improvements to the research of Julesz and Tyler. Baccei and Smith invented a new, sophisticated, full-color stereogram program in combination with state of the art 3D modeling software and colorful art techniques, and developed a totally new patented art form…MAGIC EYE®!

Magic Eye Inc. would like to thank our agents at Tenyo, a Japanese magic company, for their insight and dedication to Magic Eye 3D Images in 1991. They believed so strongly in our product that sales representatives literally stood on soapboxes on street corners to show the general public how to see our 3D Images. Then they directed interested viewers to shops where they could purchase our products. Our first Magic Eye book became a best-seller within weeks.

After creating two best-selling books in Japan, Baccei and Smith created *Magic Eye: A New Way of Looking at the World.* It was published in the United States by Andrews McMeel Publishing.

Magic Eye books ignited the worldwide stereogram explosion of the 1990's, breaking best-seller list records around the world. Every week, from 1991 and into the millennium, millions of people literally "STARE" at our images on books, posters, advertisements, cereal boxes, other retail products, as well as our syndicated newspaper feature.

Magic Eye images were first released by N.E. Thing Enterprises, which reorganized in 1996 as Magic Eye Inc. Cheri Smith is now the Art Director and President of Magic Eye Inc.

In addition to providing creative entertainment, Magic Eye images have scientific uses as well. Optometrists and eye specialists report that by viewing Magic Eye images you may improve your eyesight. In Japan, viewing Magic Eye images to improve and strengthen eyesight is currently a phenomenon. Our Japanese #1 best-selling book *Miru Miru Maga Yokunaru Magic Eye* ignited this interest back in 2001.

Magic Eye Inc. would like to take this opportunity to thank all of you for purchasing our products and for entertaining us with thousands of wonderful letters and emails. Our Magic Eye family-oriented web site receives over 40,000 visitors a week. Fun and informative: learn the science and history behind Magic Eye images and techniques, enter our contest, view our "Image of the Week", laugh at our "Joke of the Week", find out "What's New" and view current products we have in stock at our on line mail order store.

If you are viewing Magic Eye for the first time, be sure to follow the instructions on our Viewing Techniques page, and most importantly, have fun!

And as always, special thanks to artists Andy Paraskevas, Bill Clark and Ron Labbe.

www.magiceye.com

VIEWING TECHNIQUES

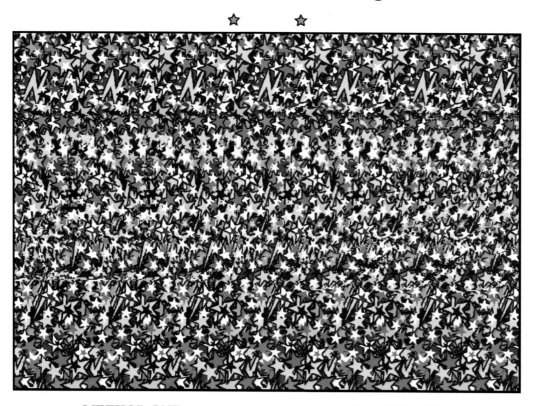

METHOD ONE

To reveal the hidden 3D illusion hold the center of this image *right up to your nose* (it should be blurry). Stare as though you are looking *through* the image. *Very very slowly* move the image away from your face until the *two stars* above the image turn into *three stars*. If you see four stars, move the image further away from your face until you see *three stars*. If you see one or two stars, start over! When you have three stars, *hold the image still* (if you are a beginner, try not to blink) and *the hidden image will slowly appear!* Once you see the hidden image and depth, you can look around the entire 3D image. The longer you look, the clearer it becomes!

METHOD TWO

Hold the center of the image *right up to your nose*. Stare as though you are looking into the distance. *Very slowly* move the image away from your face, perhaps an inch every two seconds. Keep looking through the page until you *begin to see depth*, then *hold the image still*. Discipline is needed when something starts to "come in" because at that moment you will instinctively try to look at the page rather than looking through it. If you "lose it," start again.

METHOD THREE

The cover of this book is shiny; hold it in such a way that you can identify a reflection. For example, hold it under an overhead lamp so that it catches the light. Simply look at the object you see reflected and continue to stare at it with a fixed gaze. After several seconds the reflection will appear to fade, let it! You will begin to perceive depth, followed by the 3D image, which will develop almost like an instant photo!

MORE INFORMATION

There are two methods of viewing our Magic Eye® images: crossing your eyes and diverging your eyes (focusing through the page at a distant focal point). All the pictures in this book were designed to be viewed by diverging the eyes. If you view the images by crossing your eyes, all the depth information comes out backward! If we intend to show an airplane flying in front of a cloud, if you cross your eyes, you will see an airplane-shaped hole cut into the cloud! Once you learn the method, try the other. Another common occurrence is to diverge the eyes twice as far as is needed to see the hidden image. In this case, a weird, more complex version of the intended object is seen.

One last note before you start. Although Magic Eye® is great fun at work and other entertaining social situations, those are not often the best places to learn. If you don't "get it" in two or three minutes, wait until another, quieter time. This technique is safe and has been proven to be helpful to your eyes, but don't overdo it. Straining your eyes will not help you "see," and will just make you feel uncomfortable. The key is to relax and let the image come to you.

The last pages of this book provide a key that shows the 3D picture that you will see when you find and train your MAGIC EYE®.

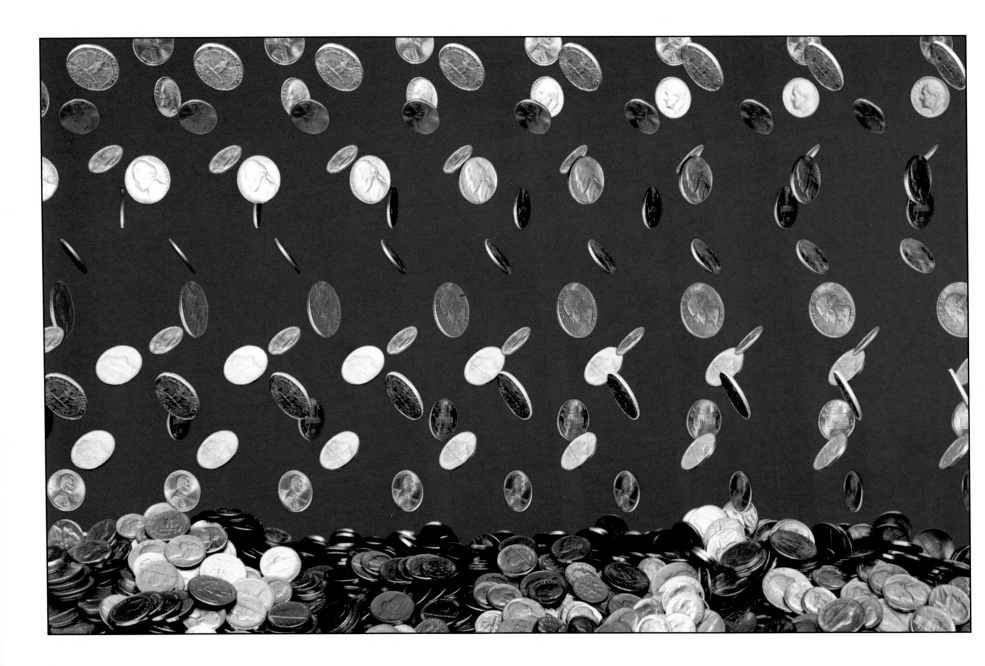

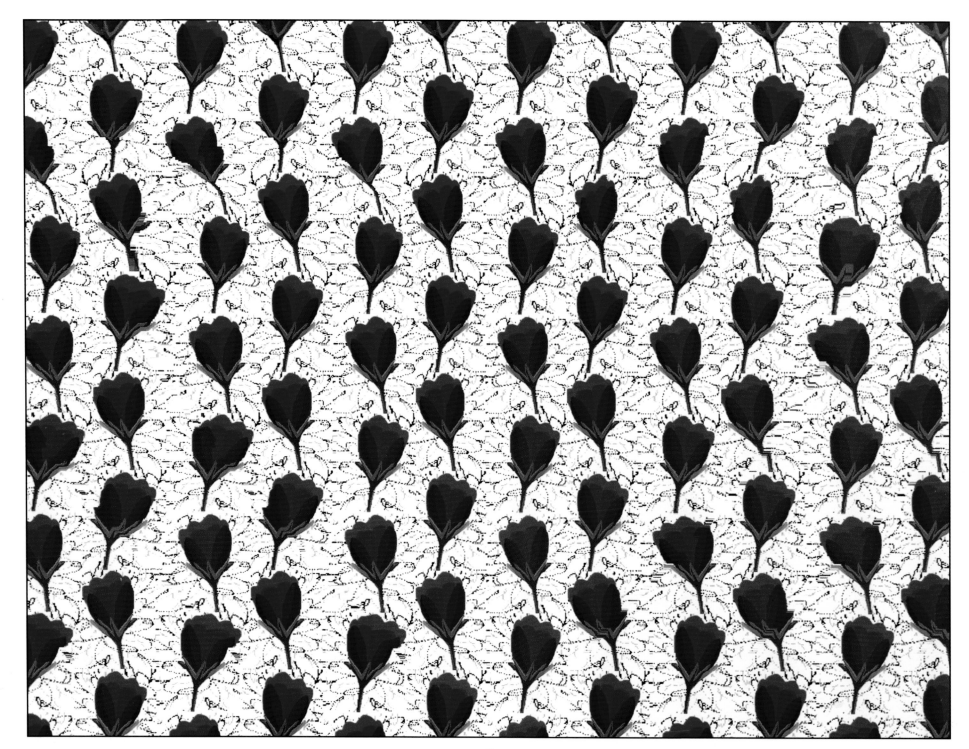

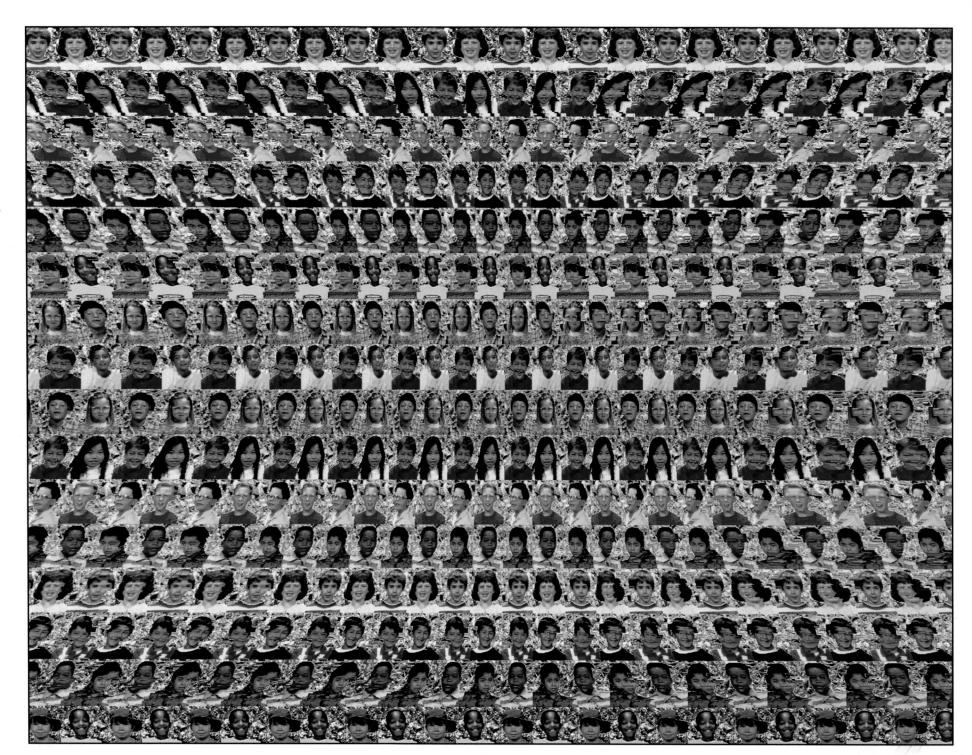

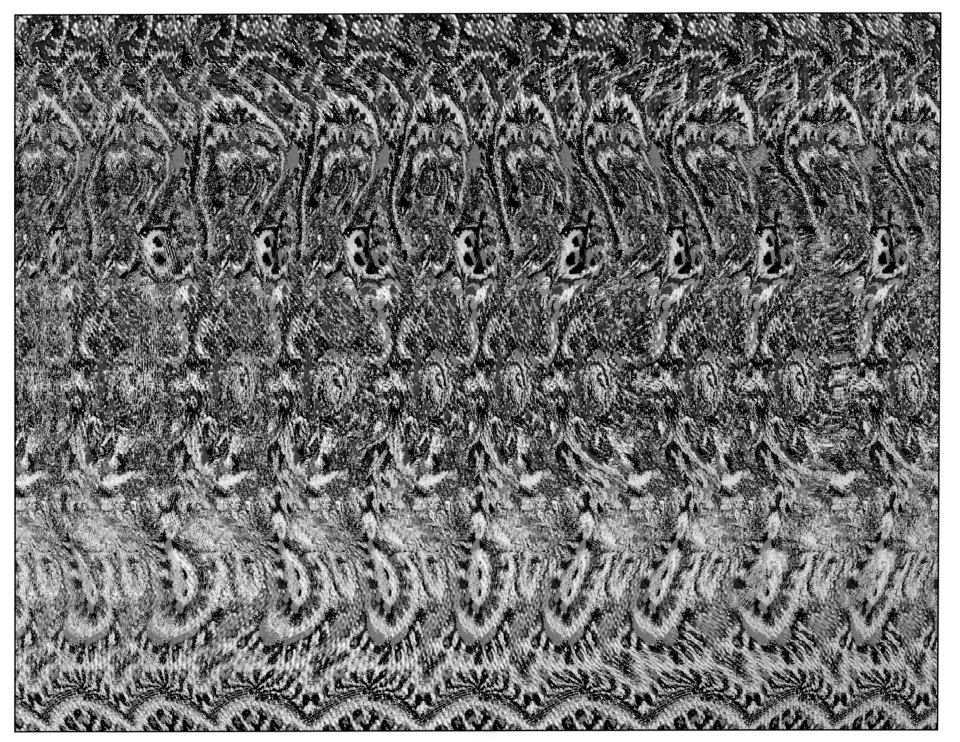

11

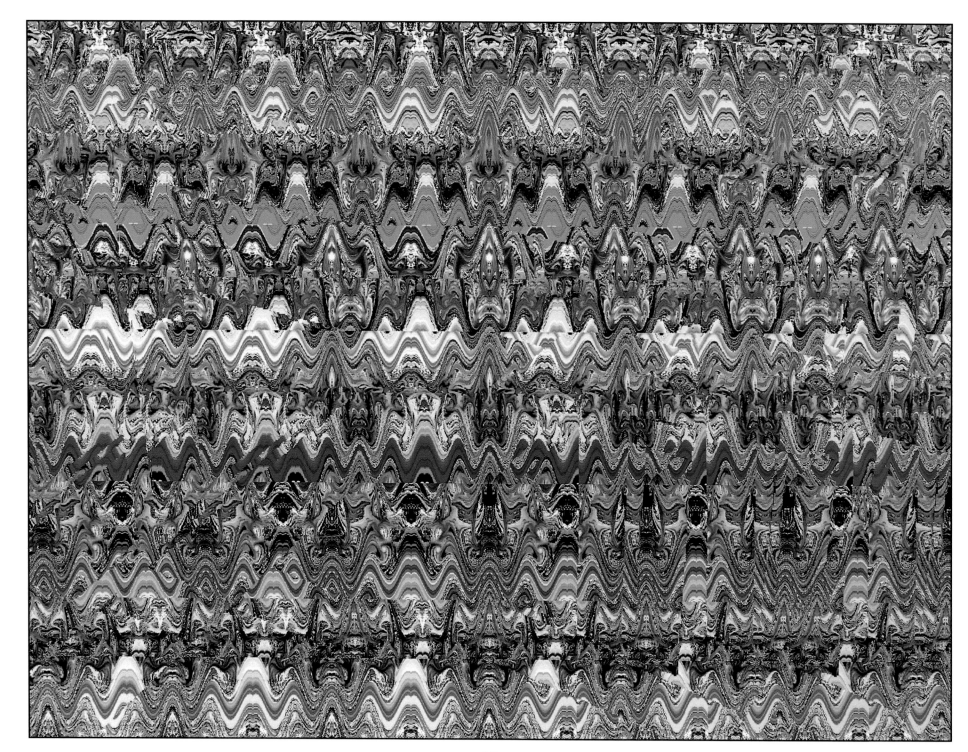

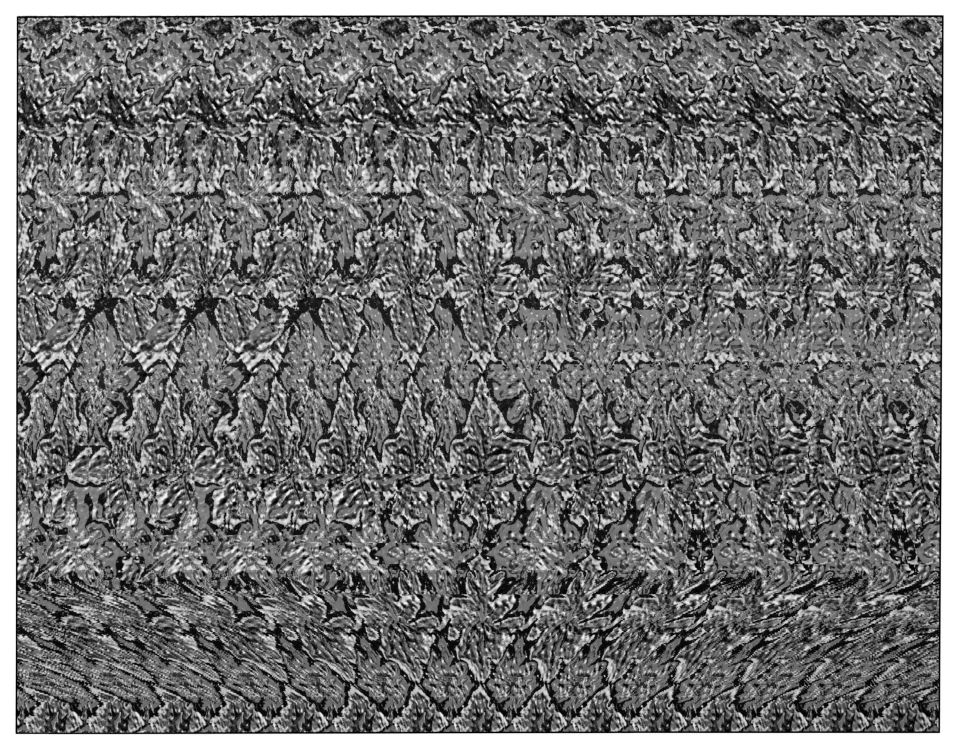

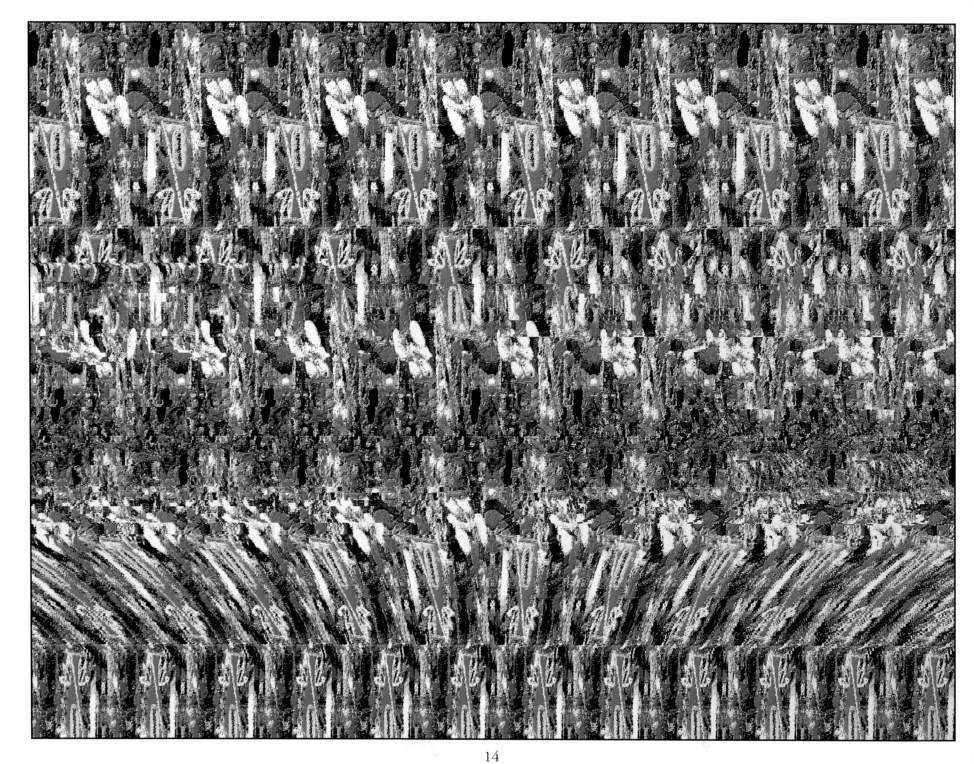

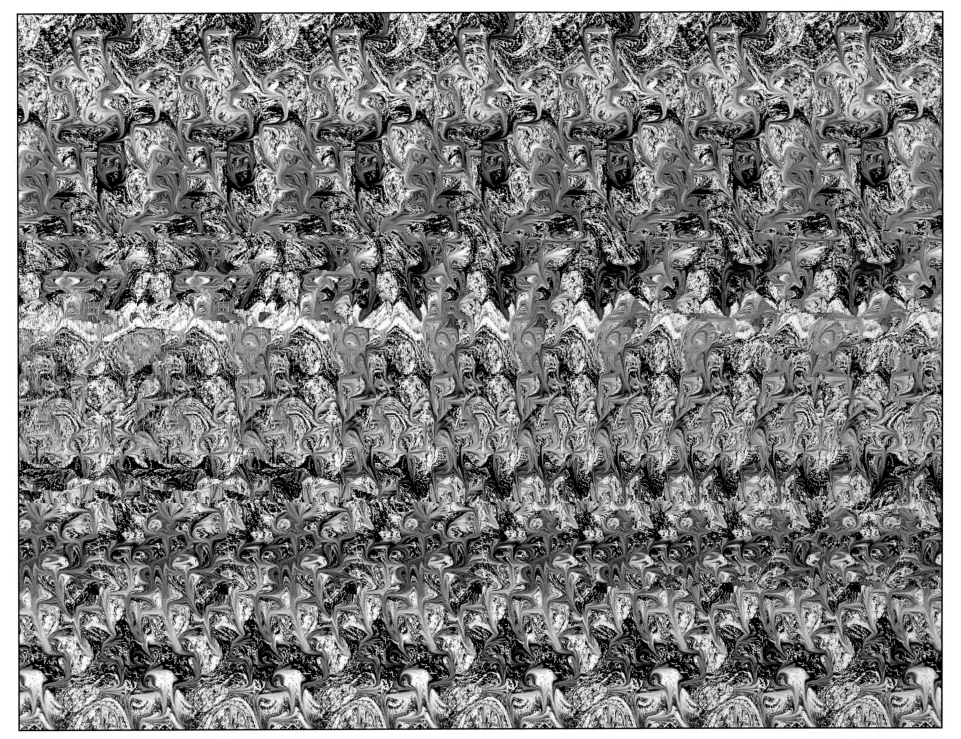

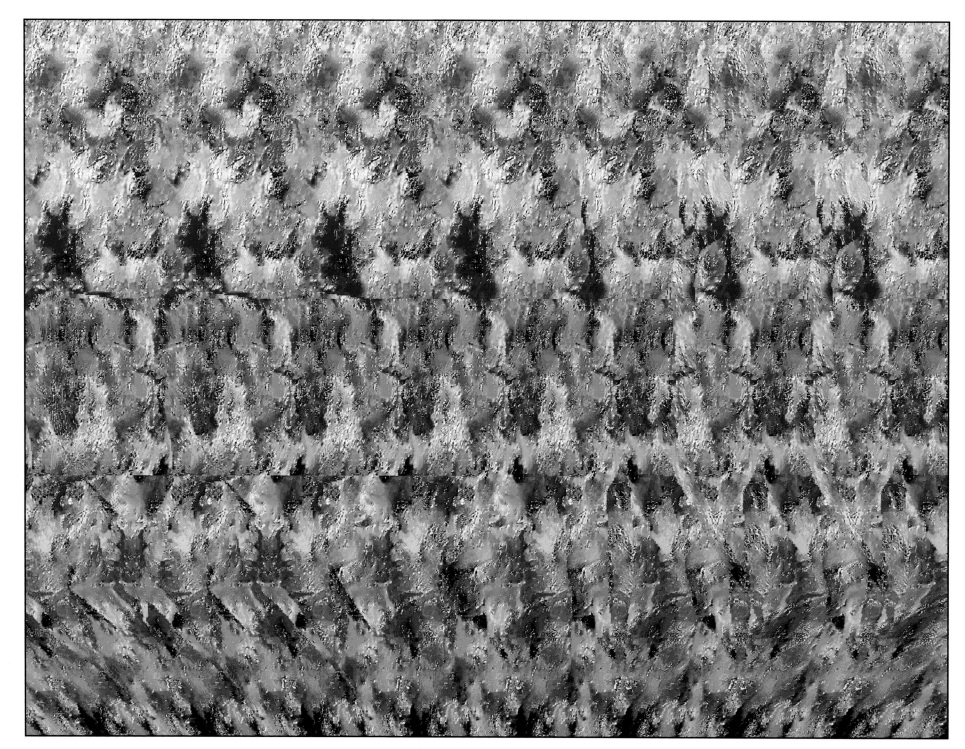

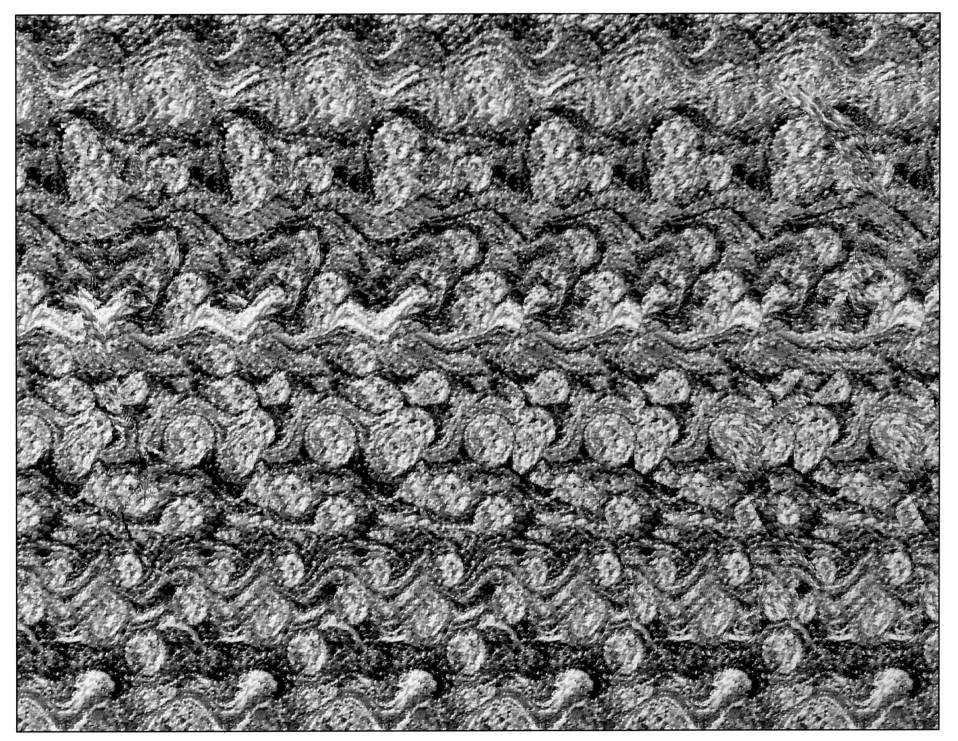

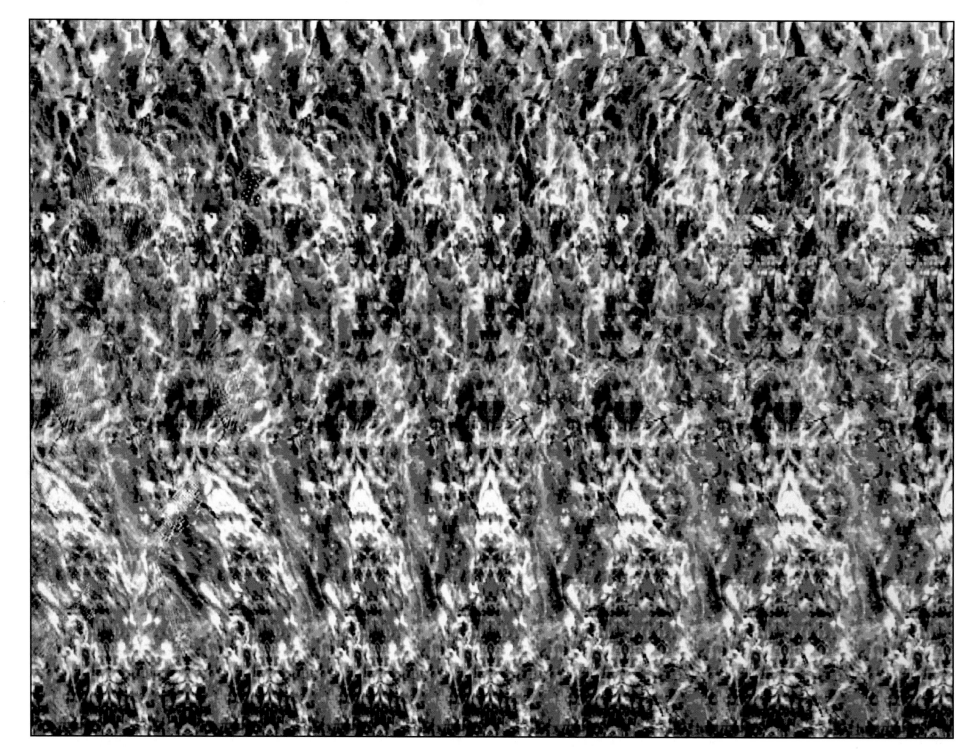

18

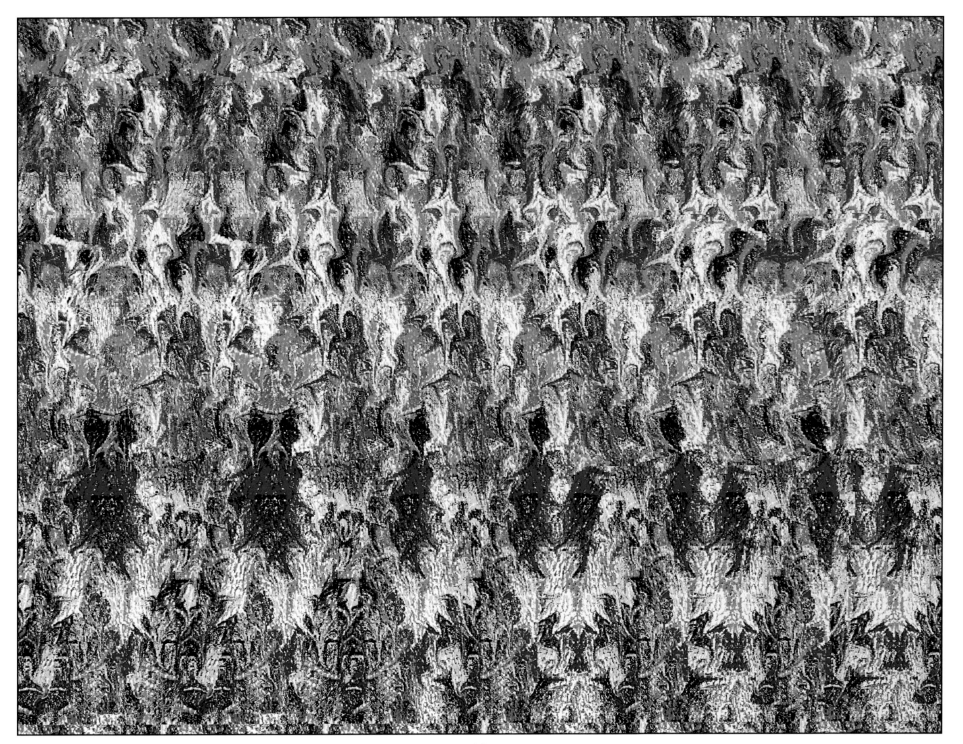

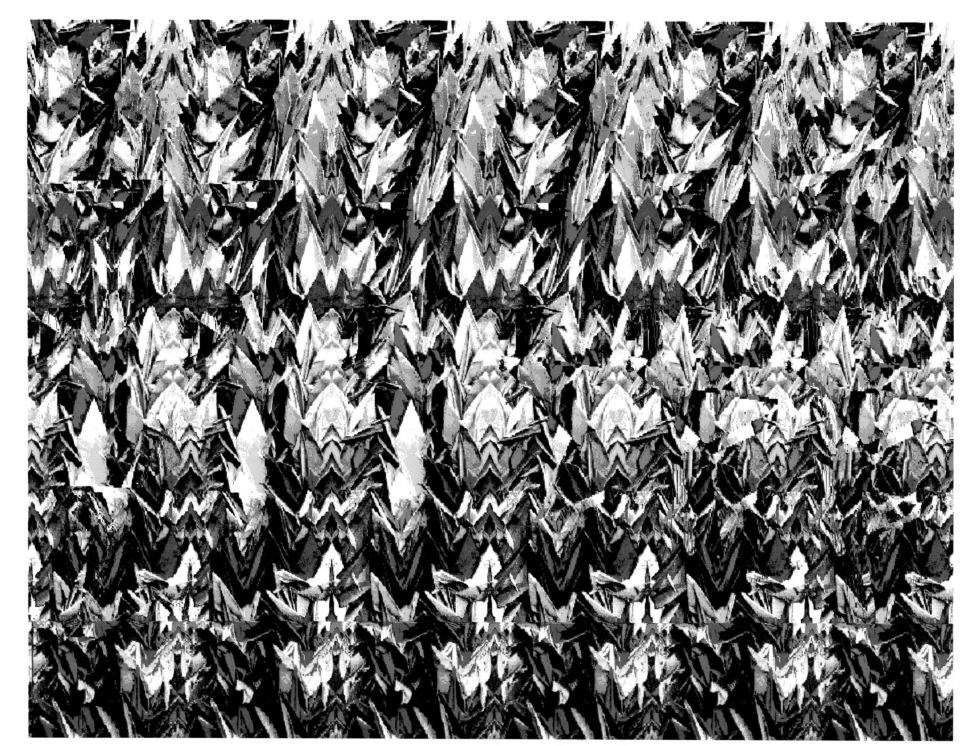

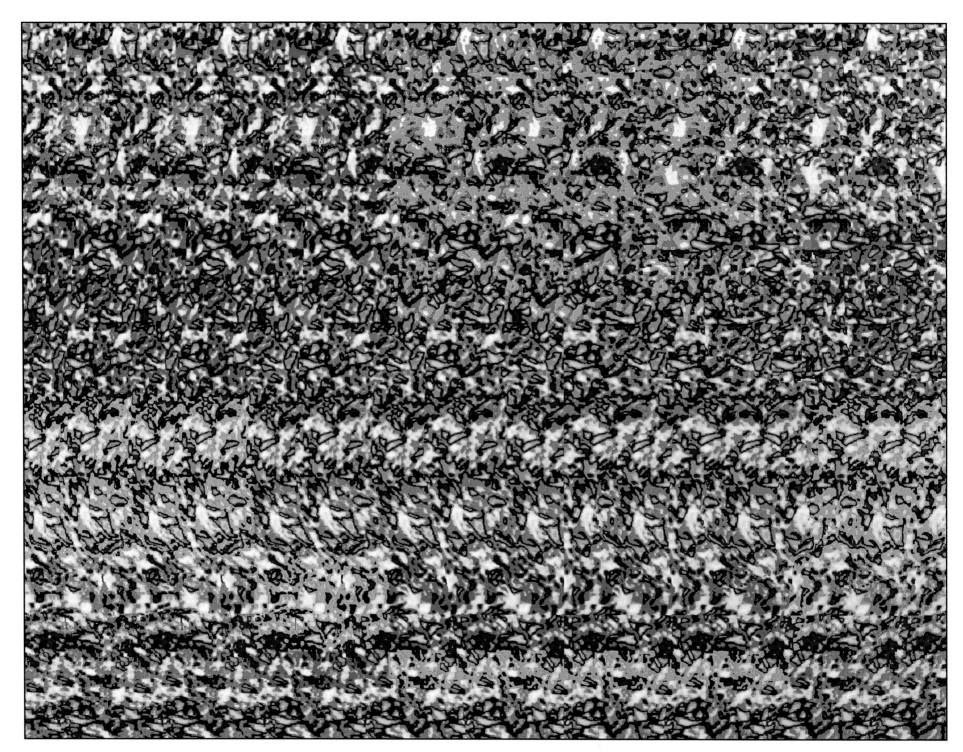

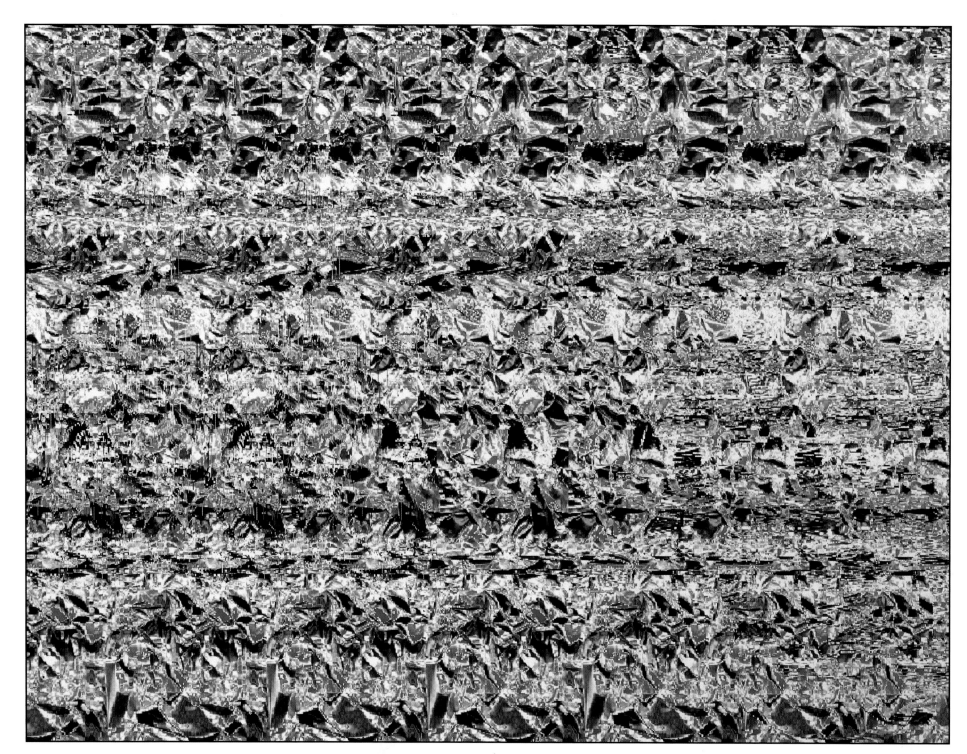

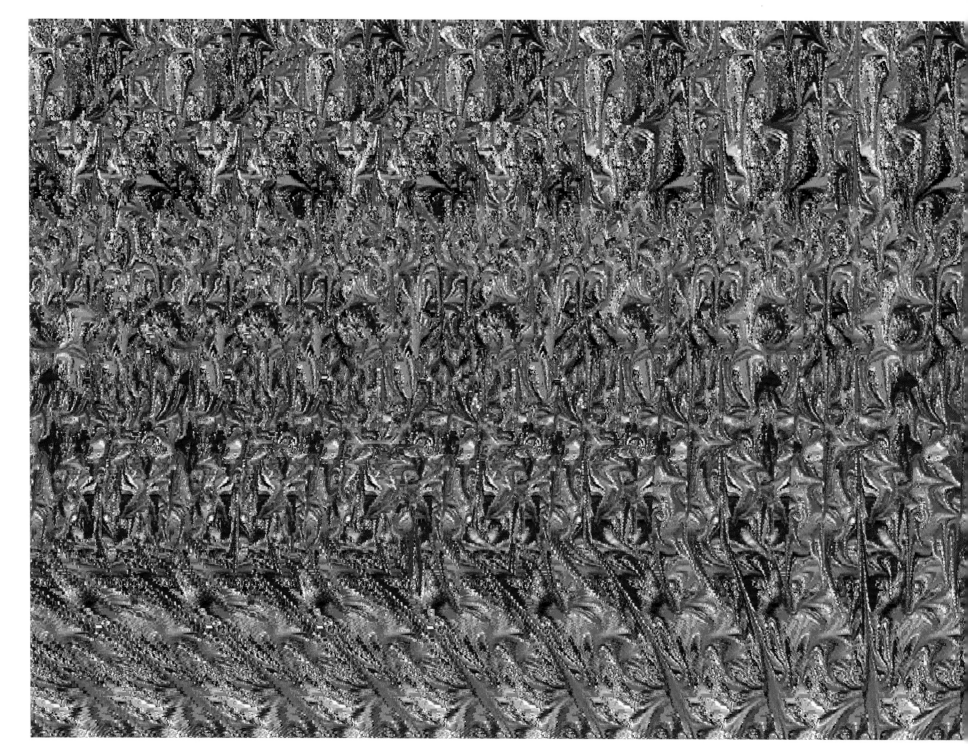

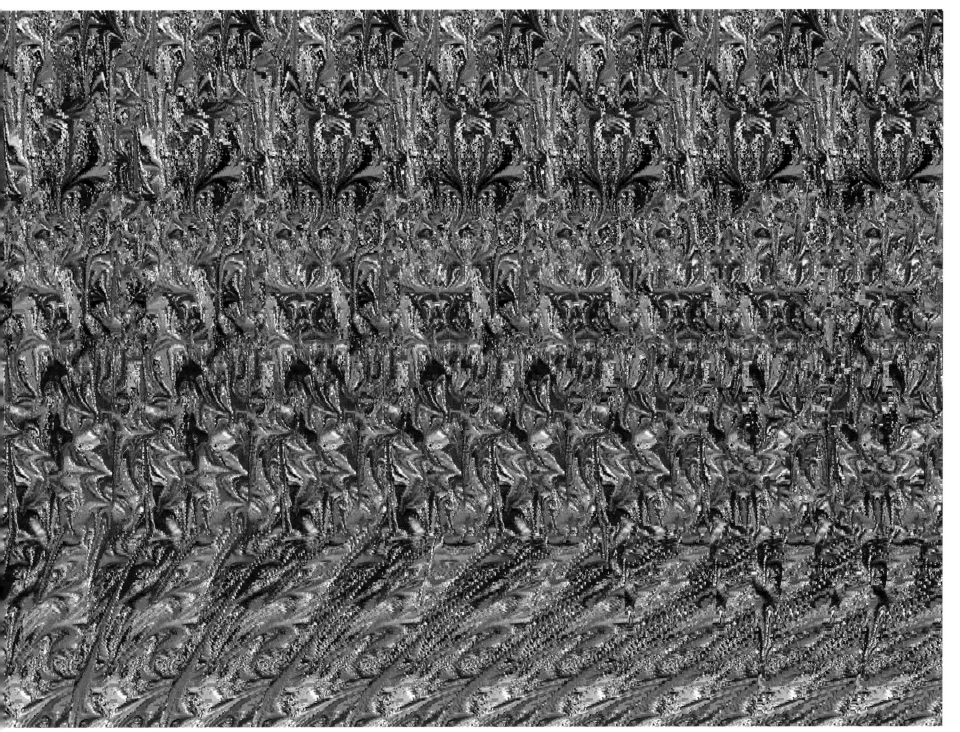

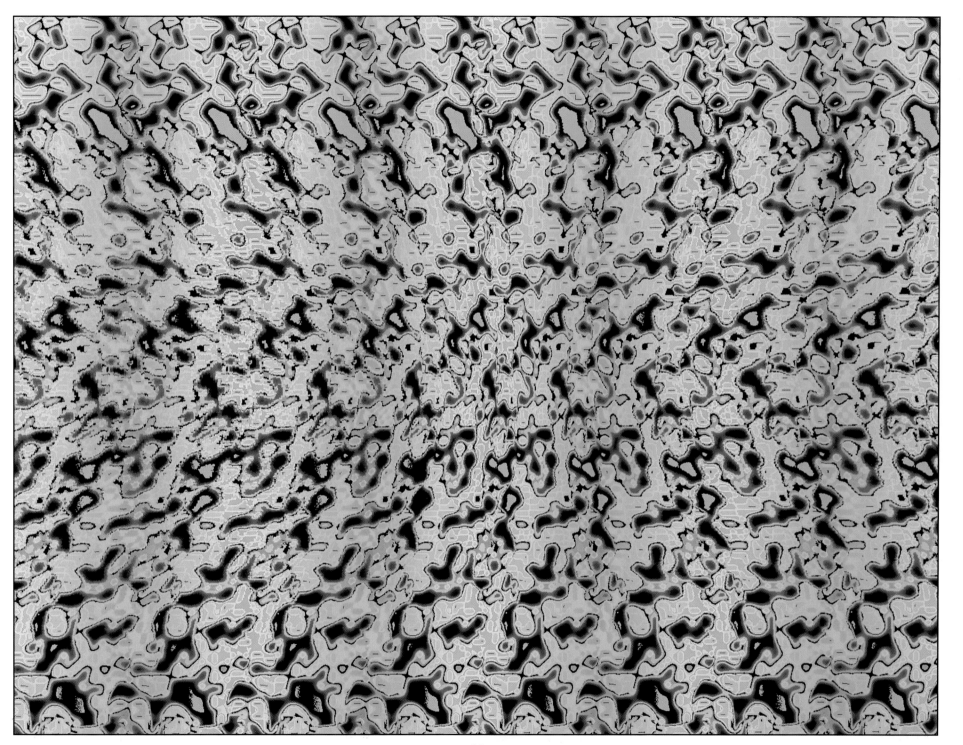

31

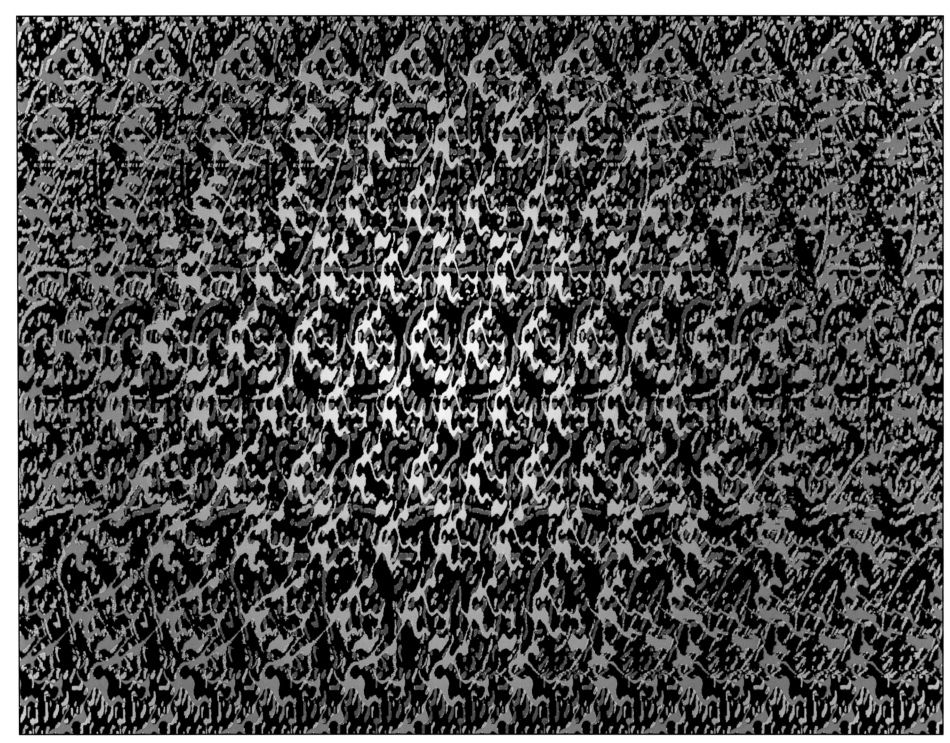

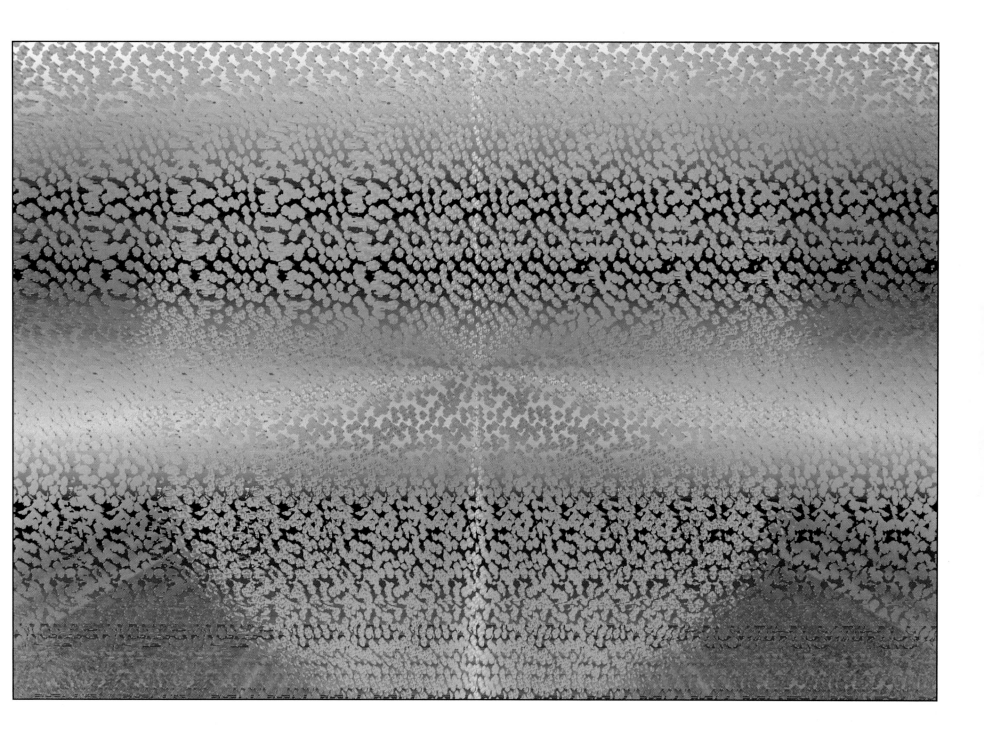

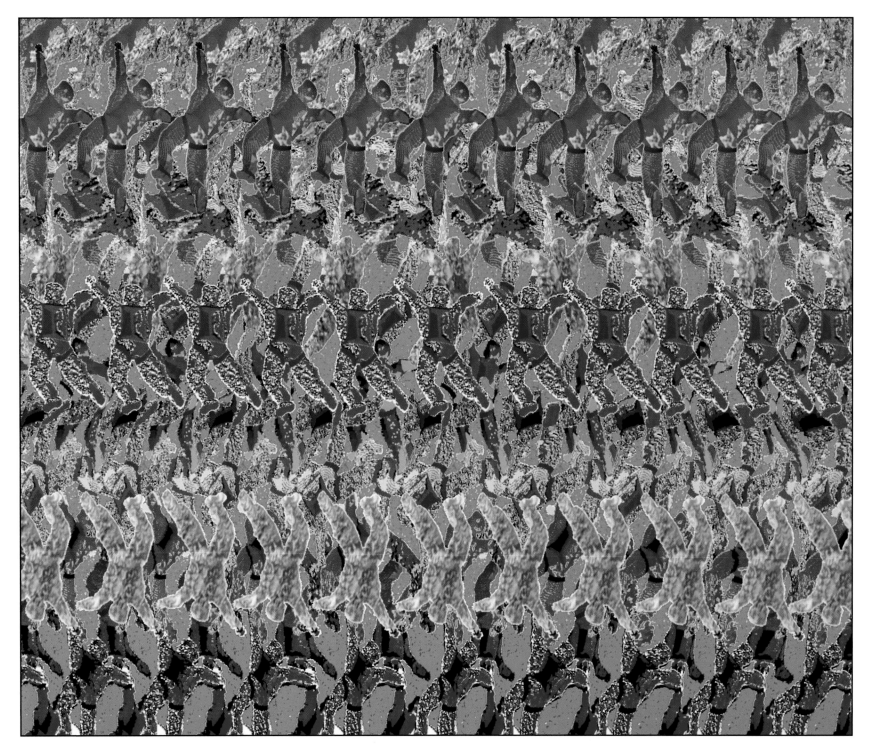

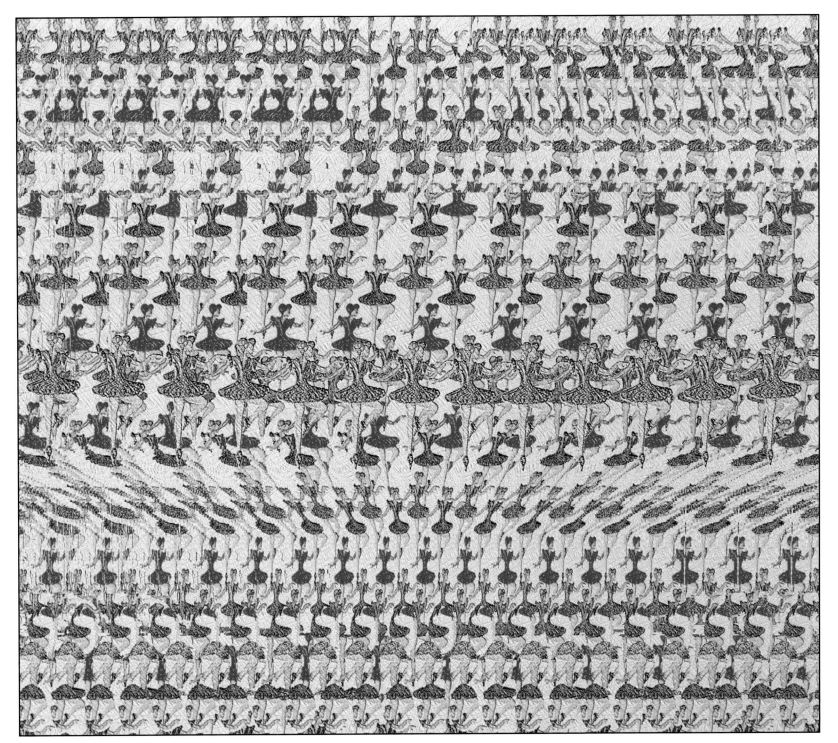

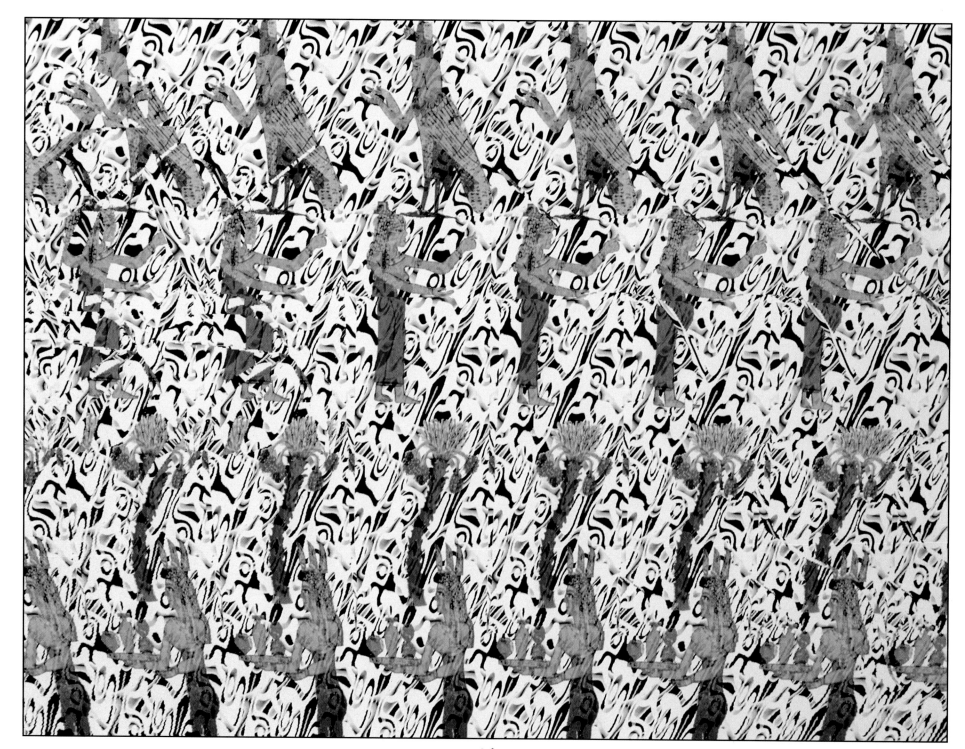

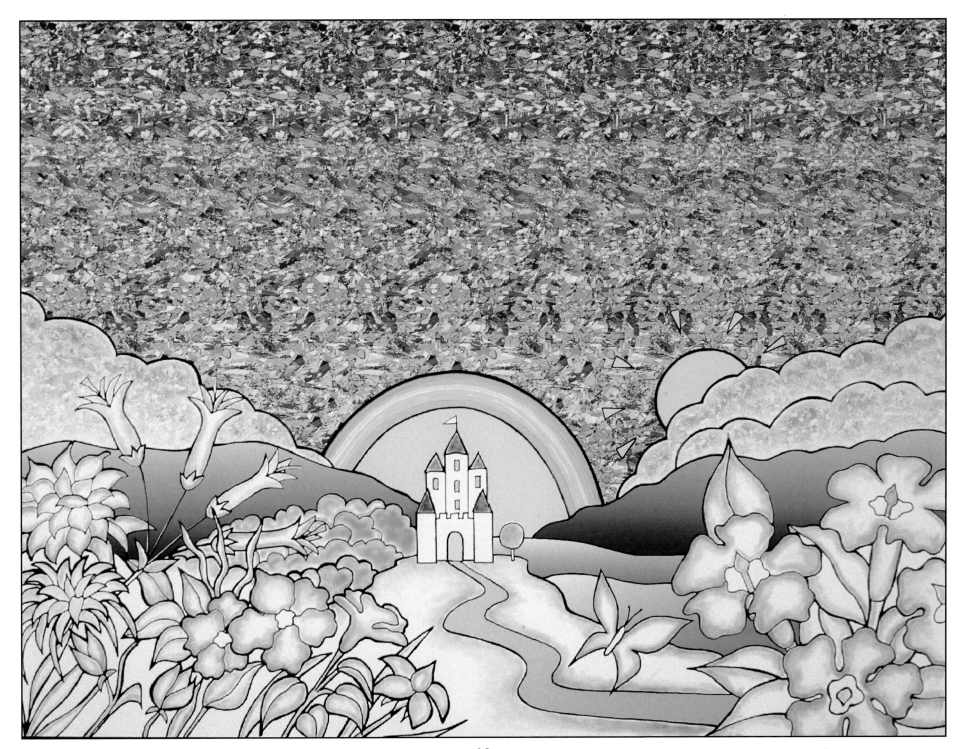

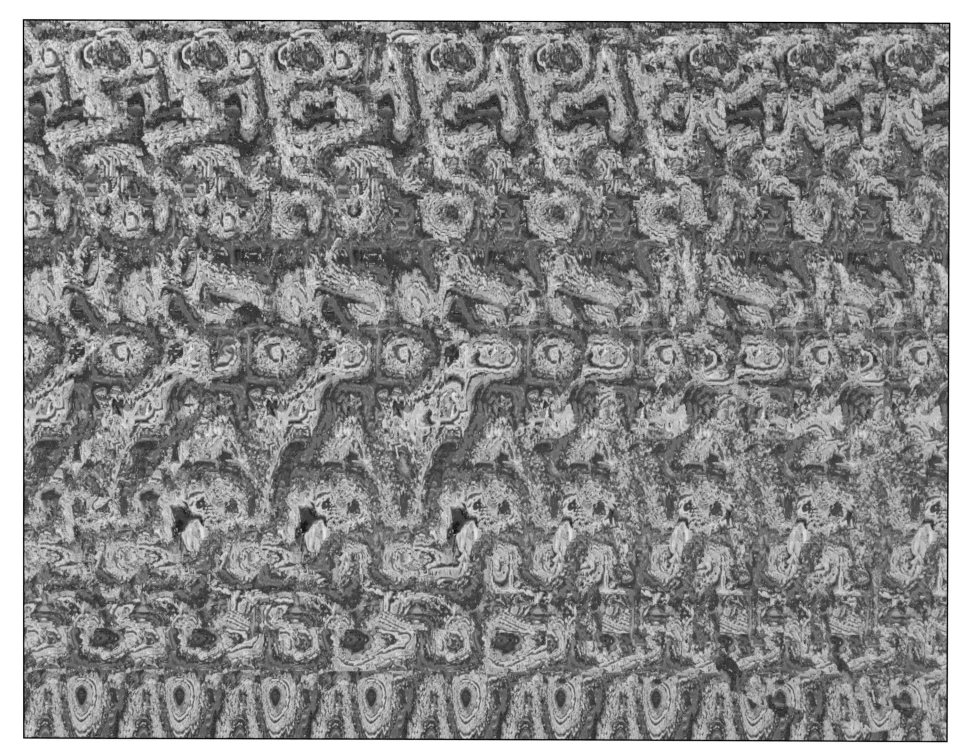

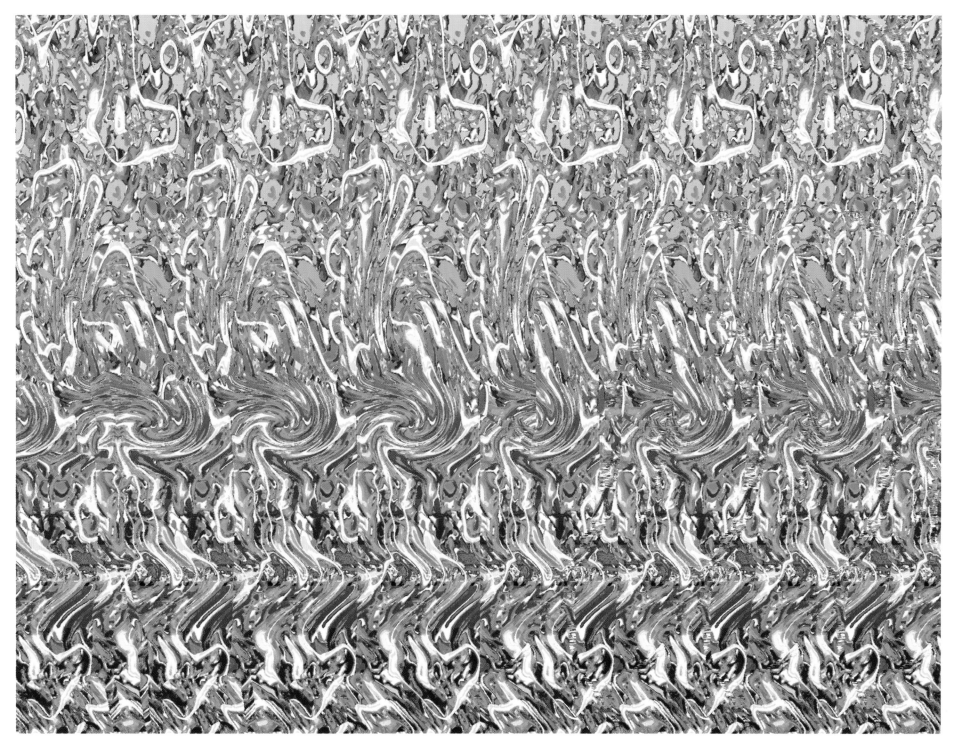

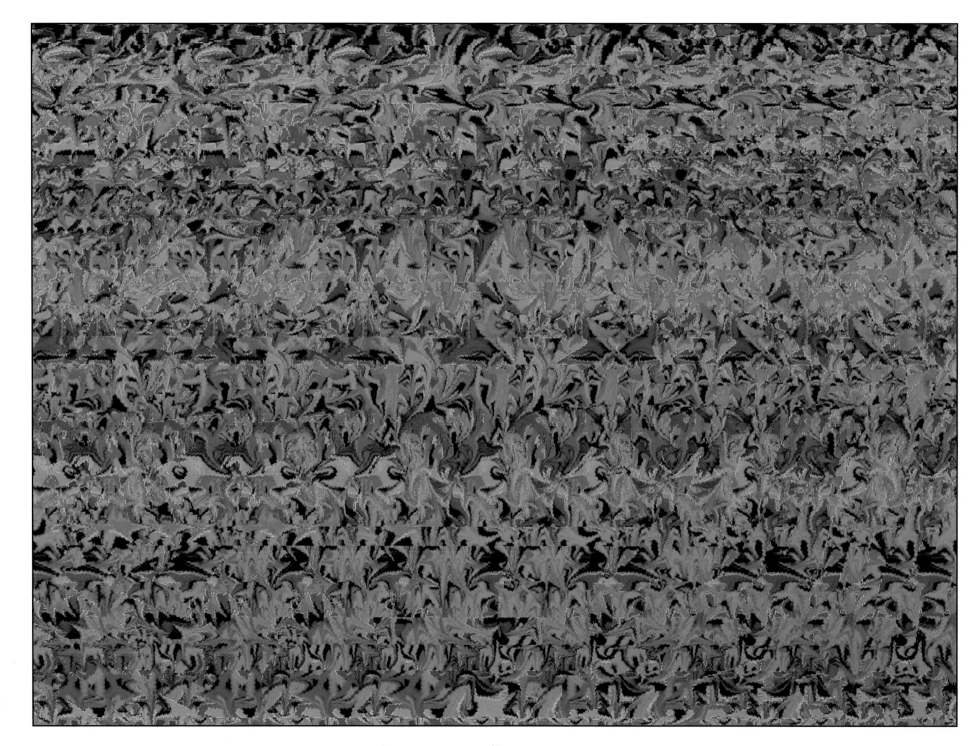

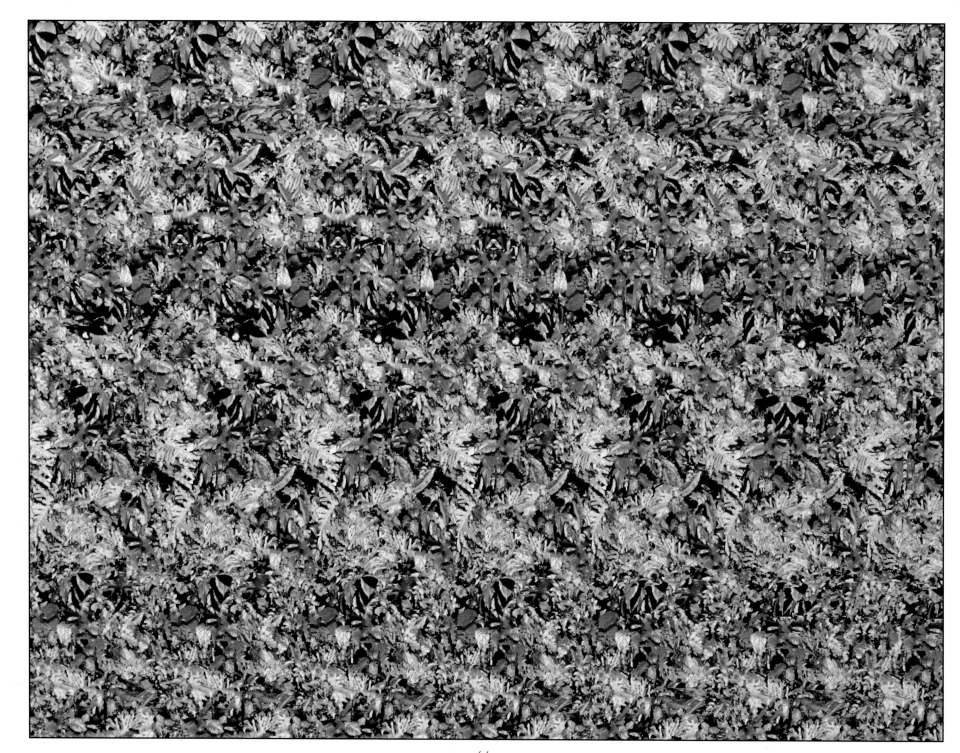

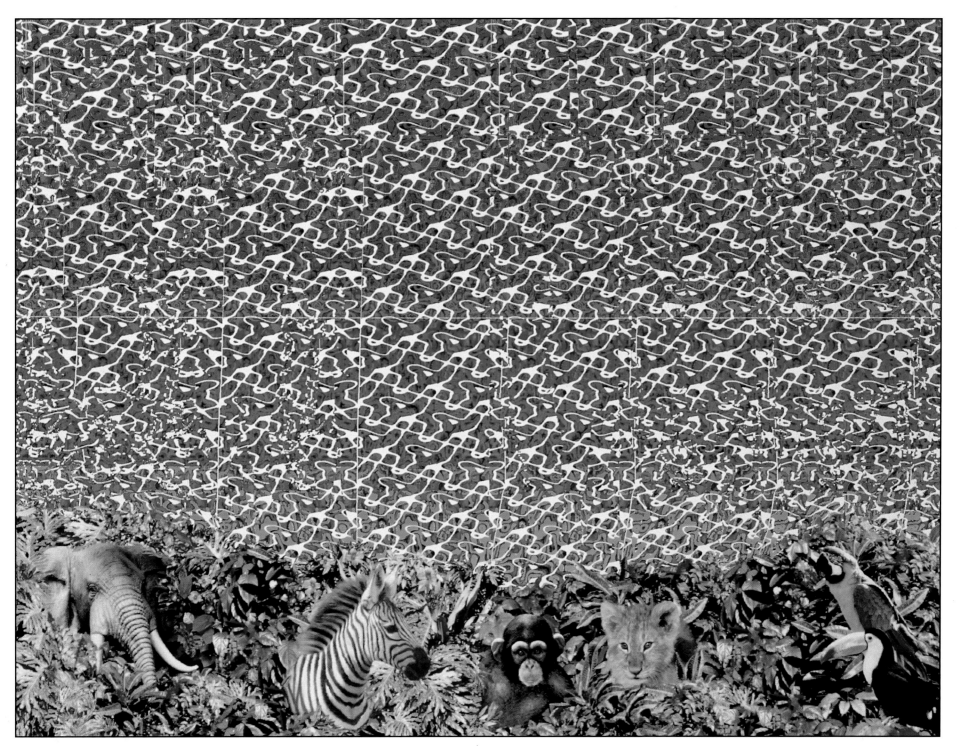

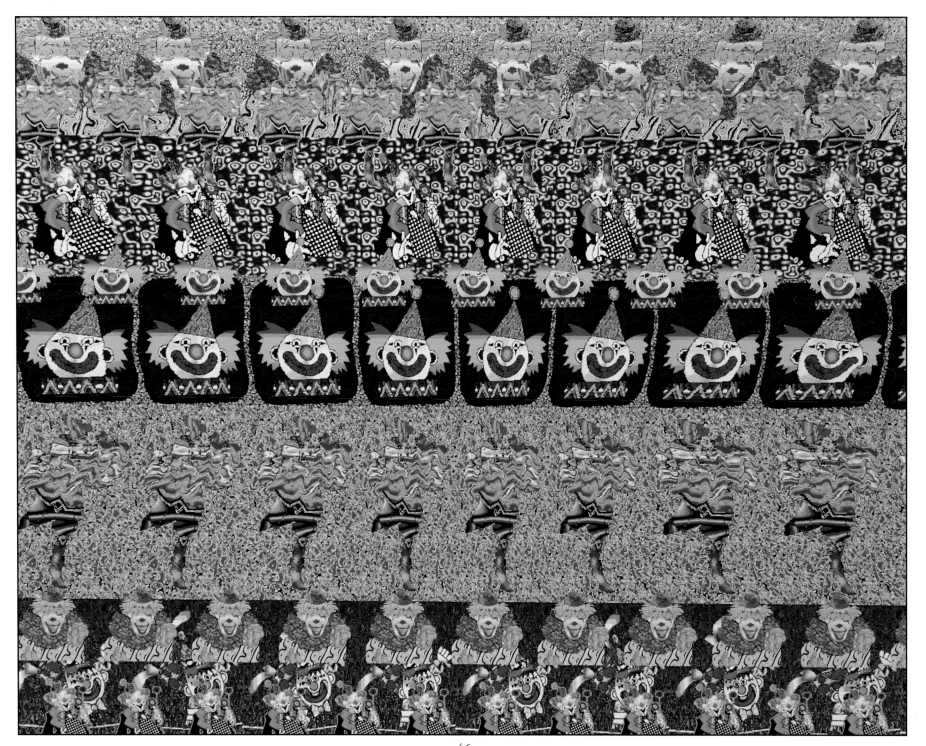

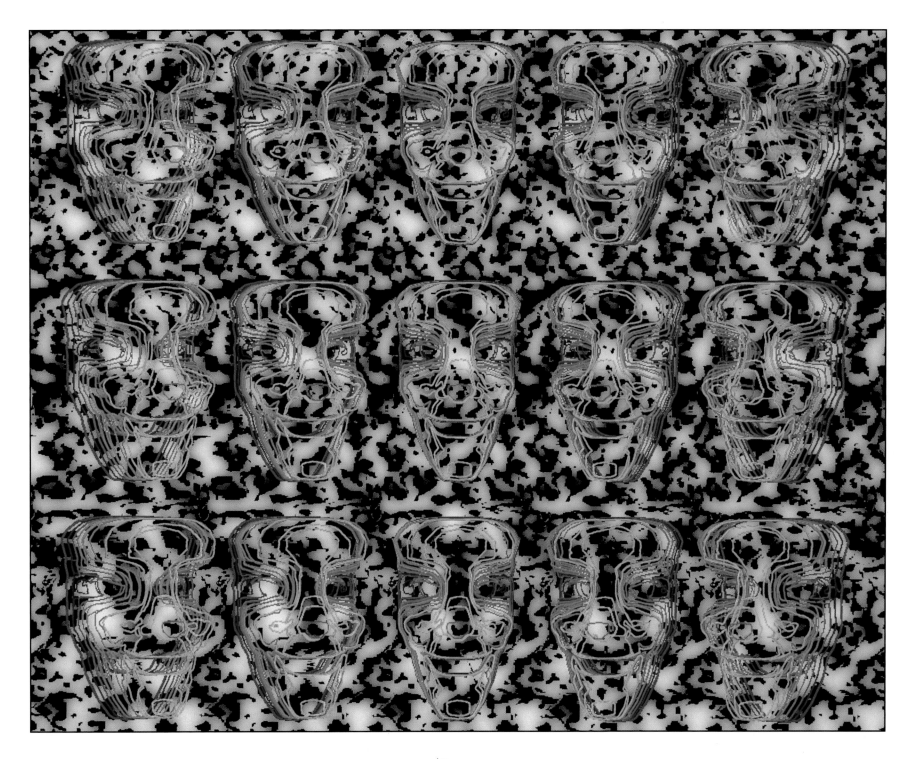

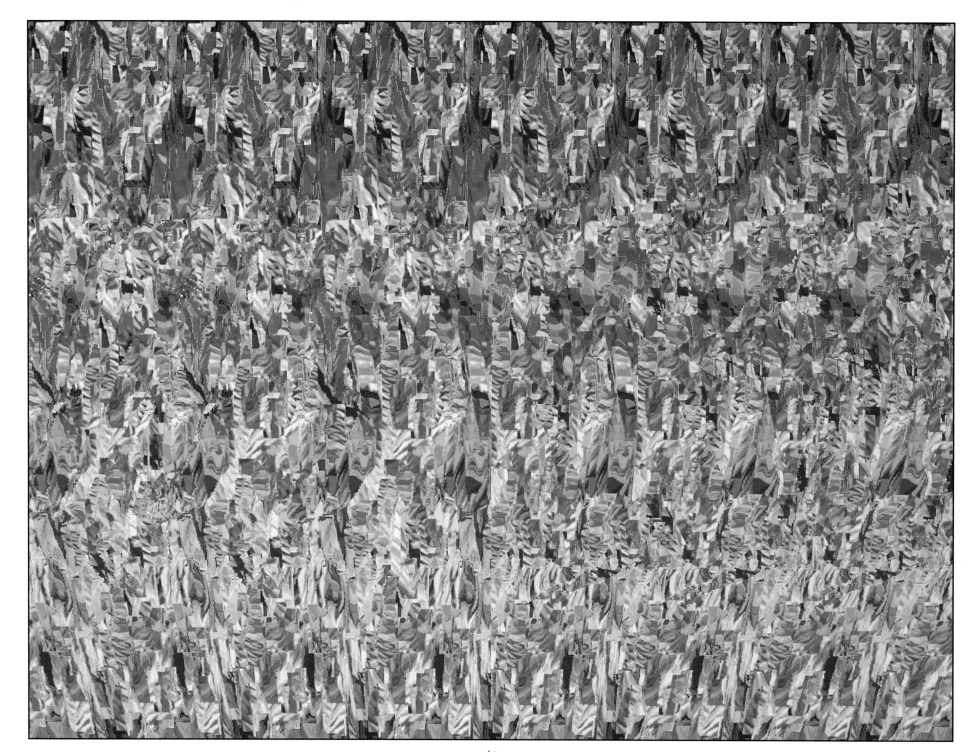

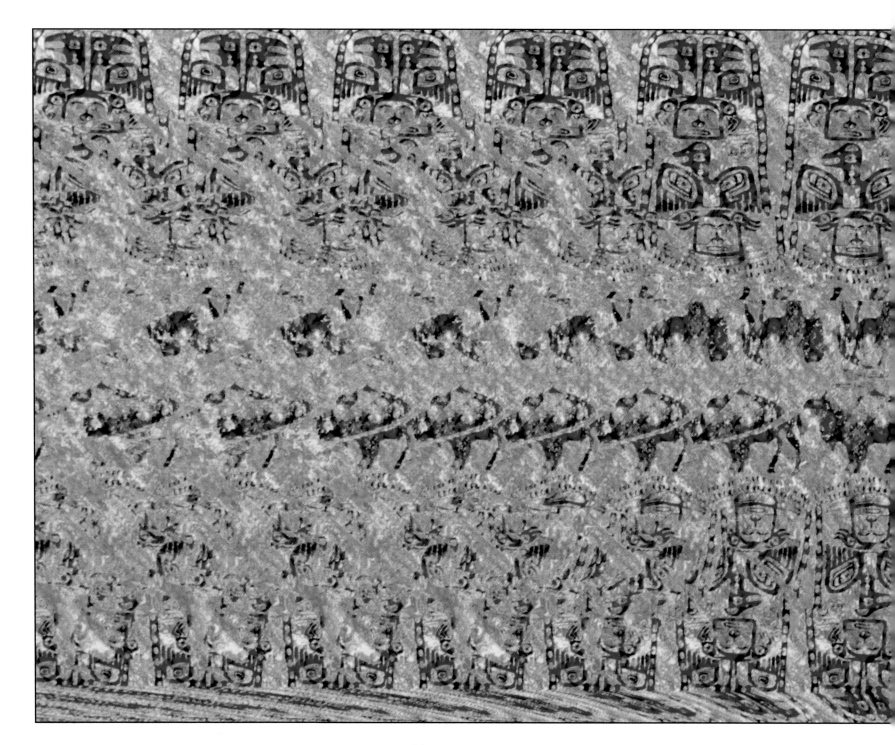

50

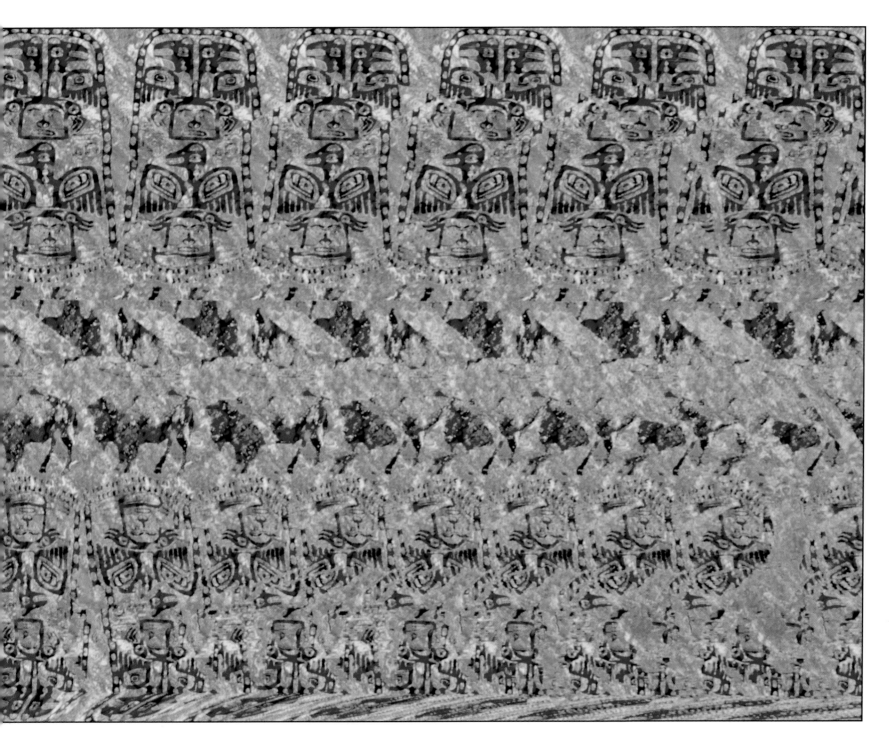

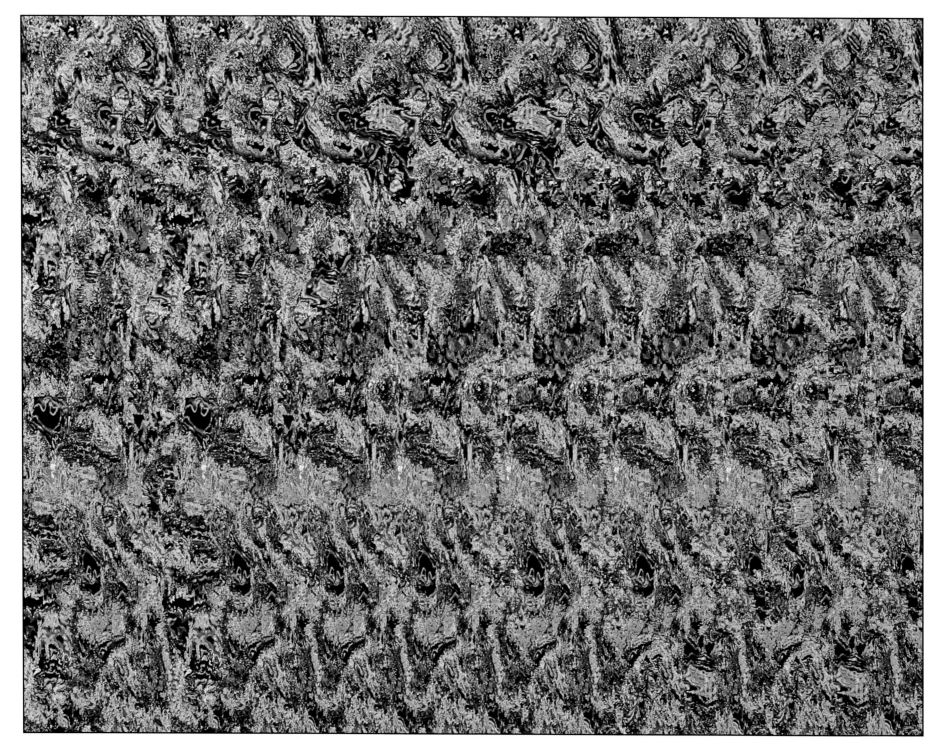

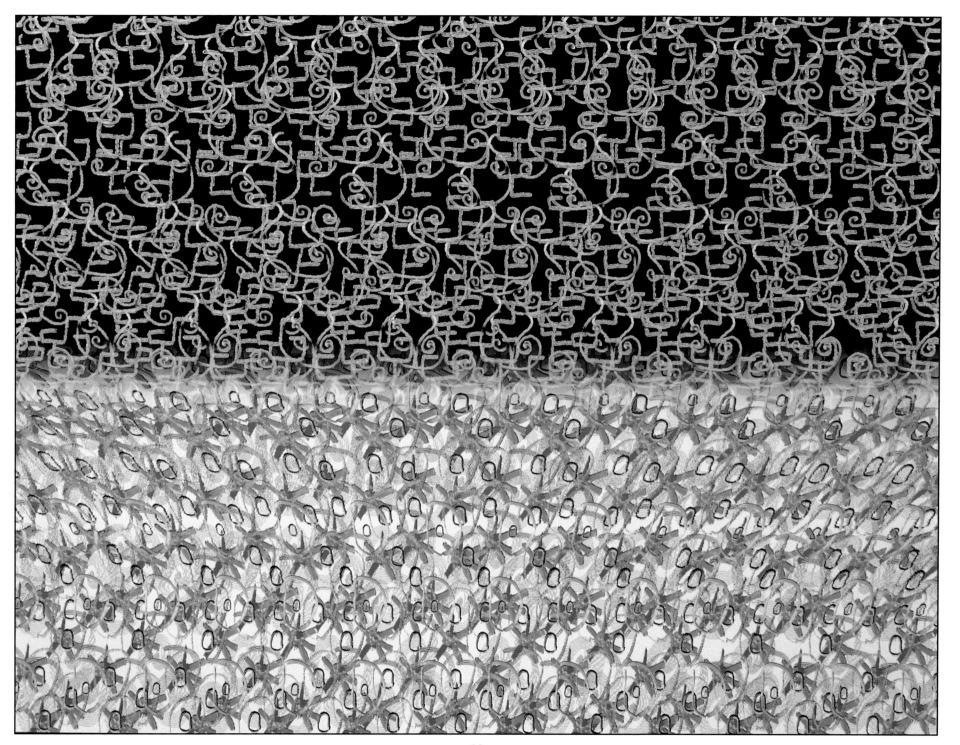

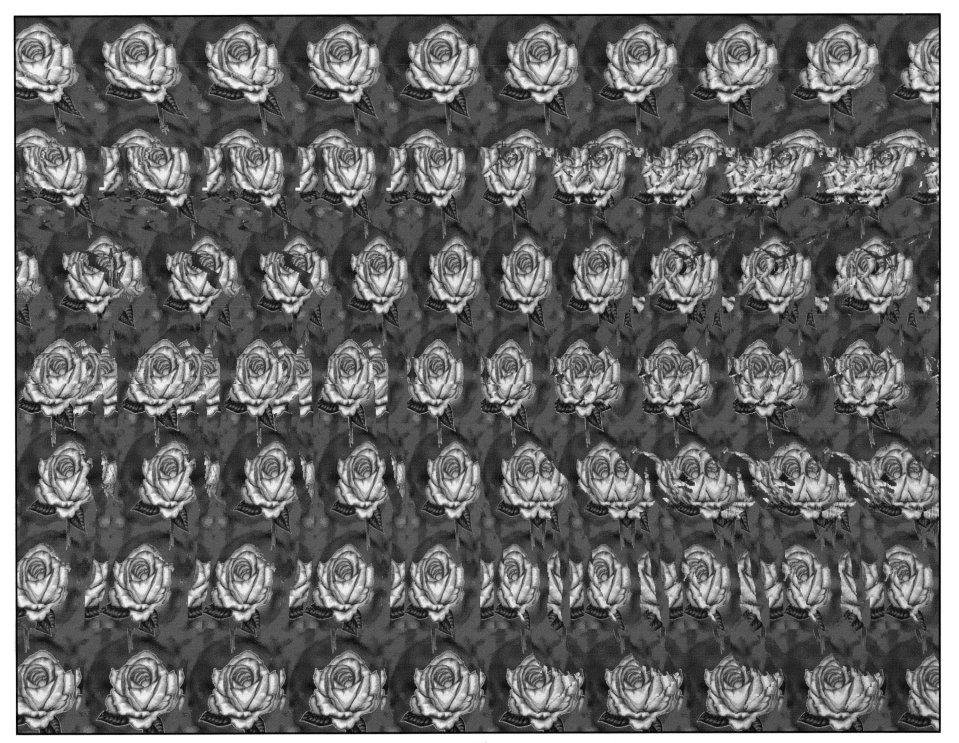

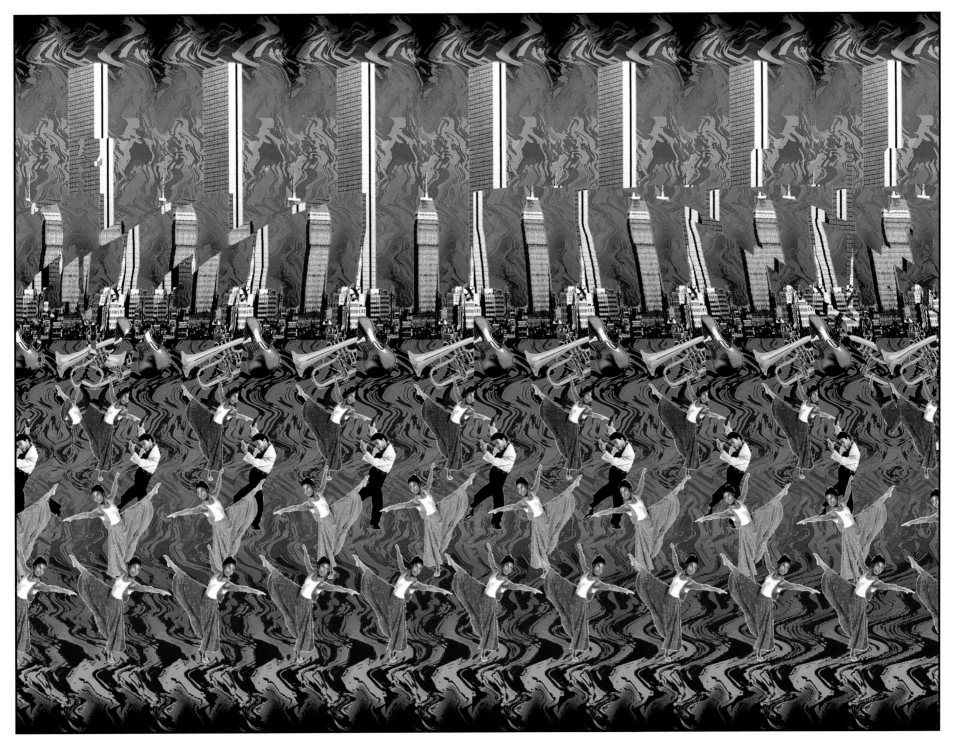

59

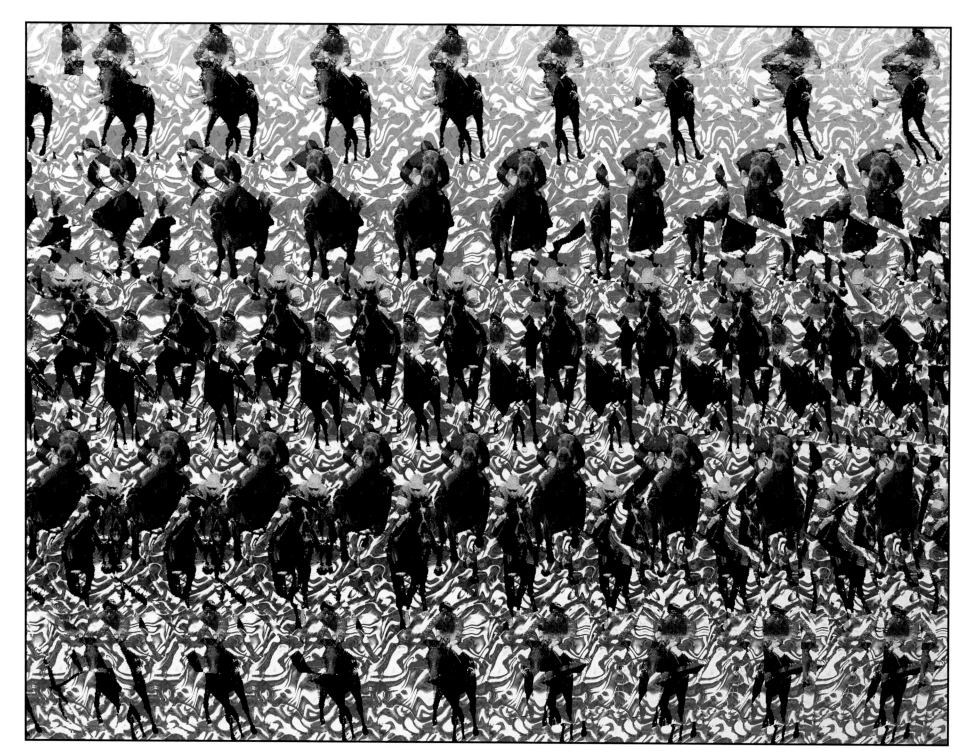

60

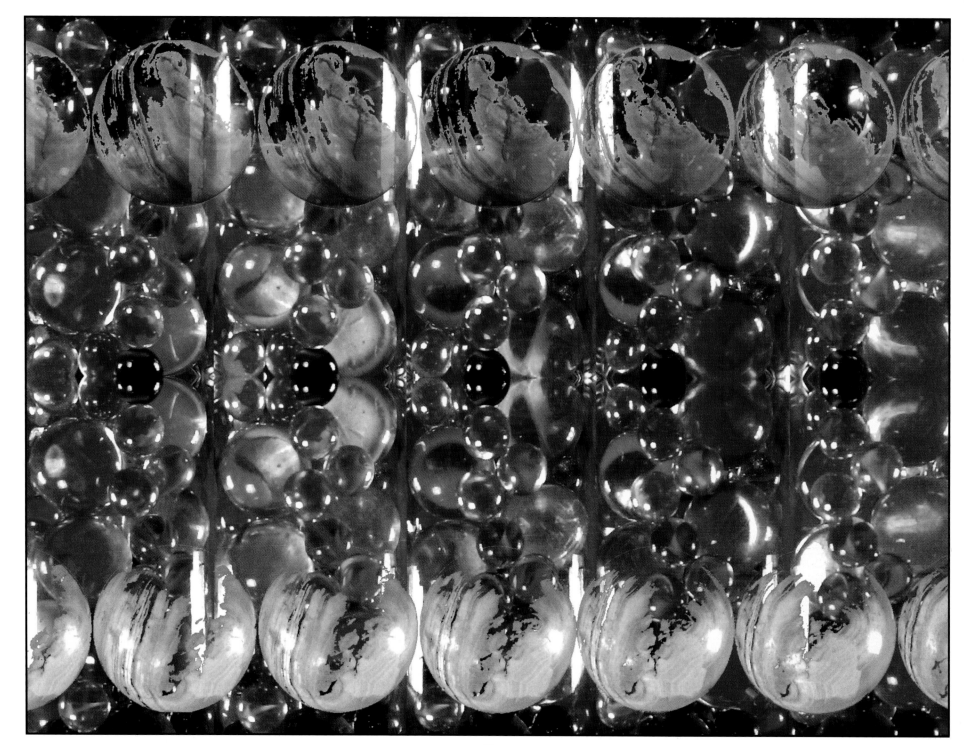

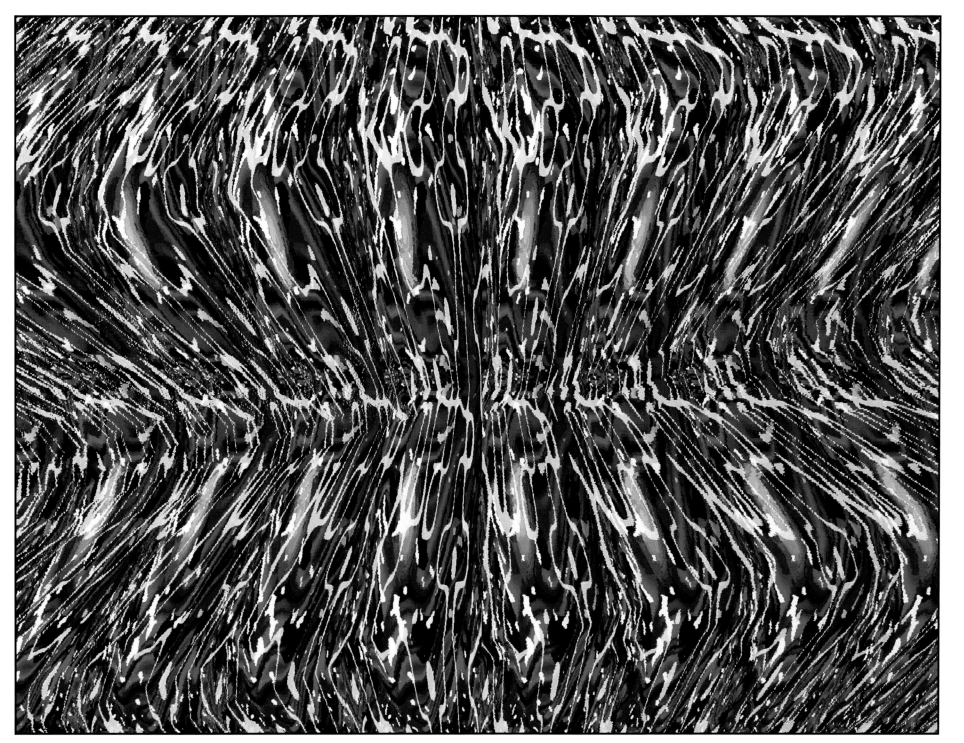

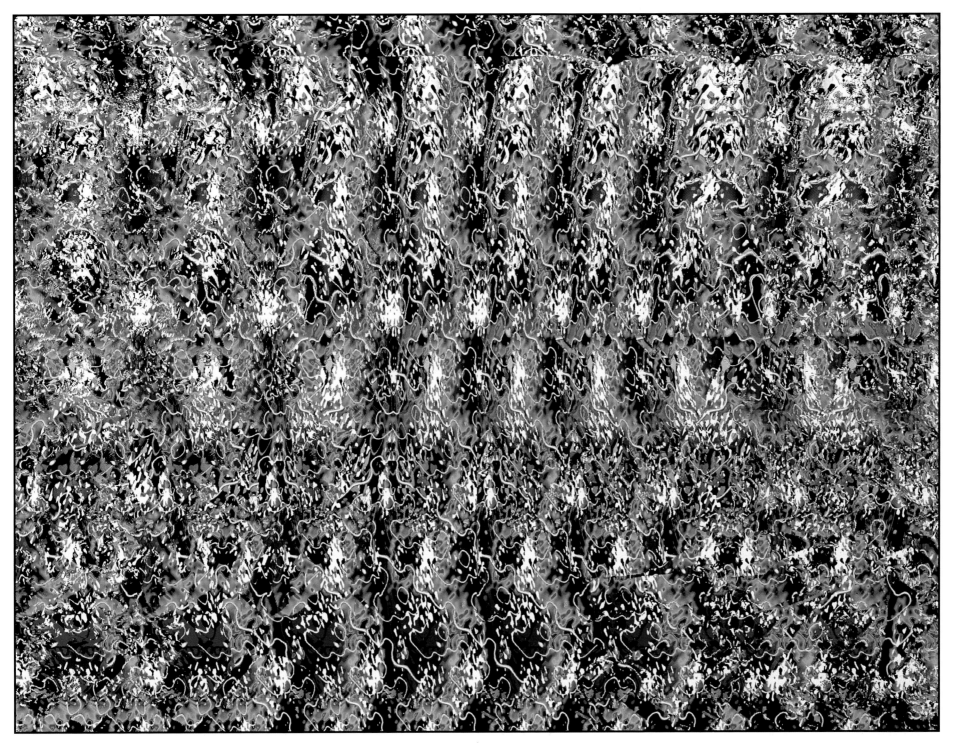

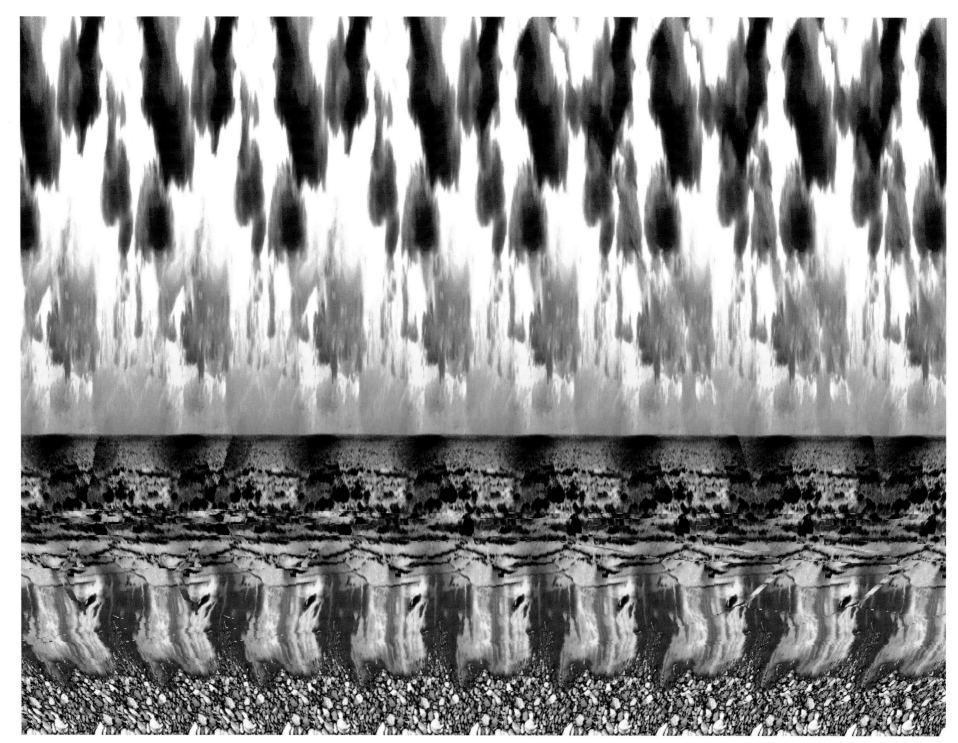

66

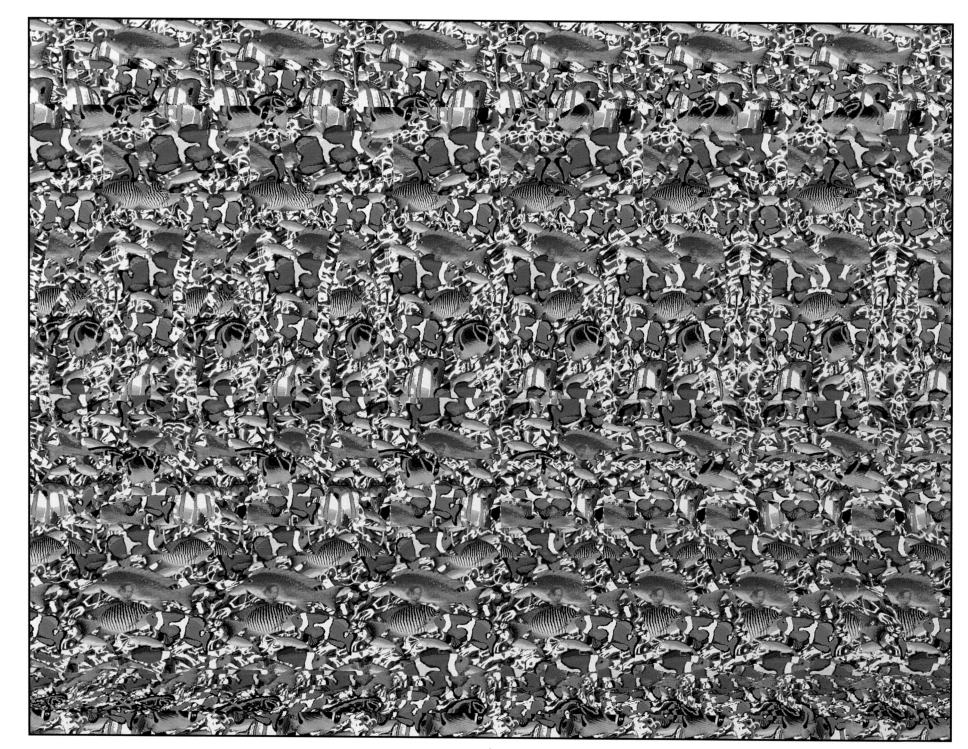

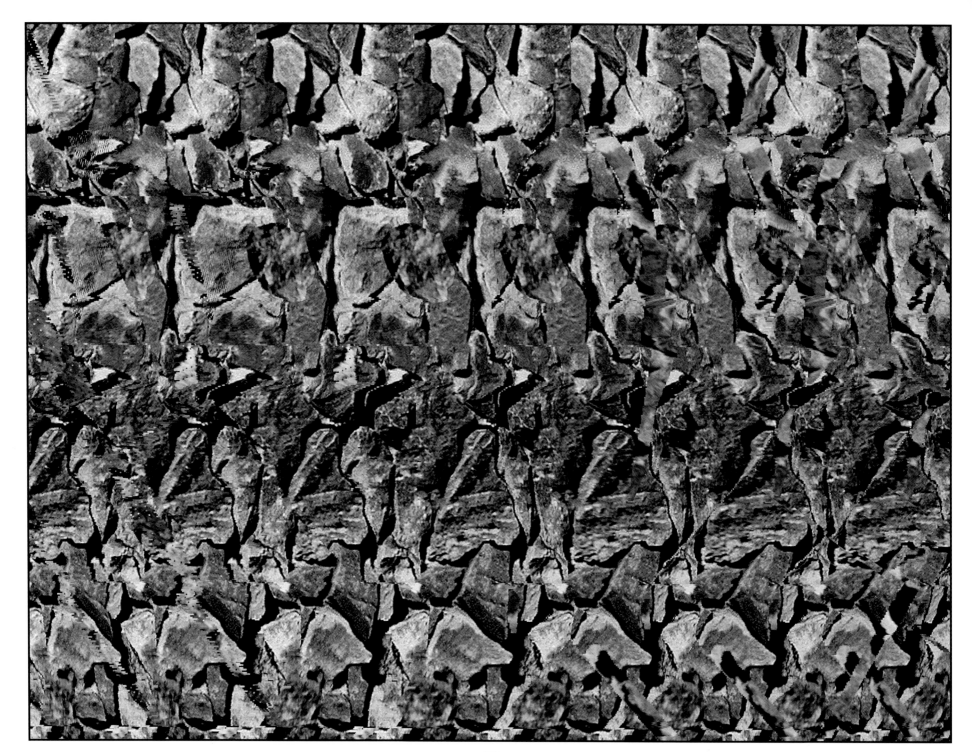

70

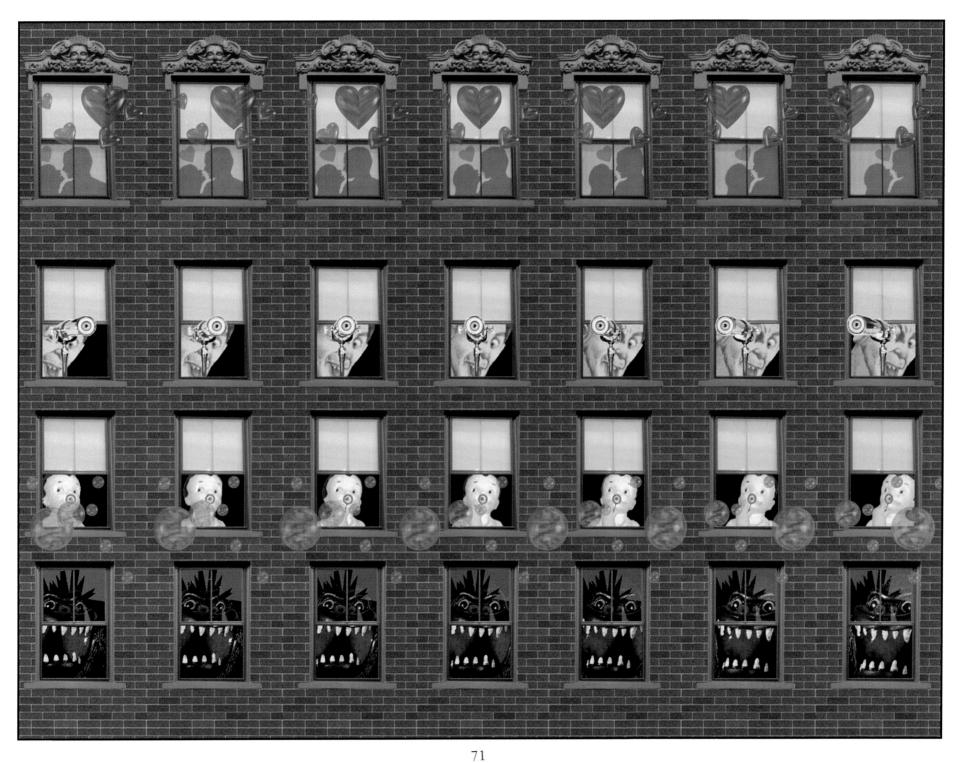

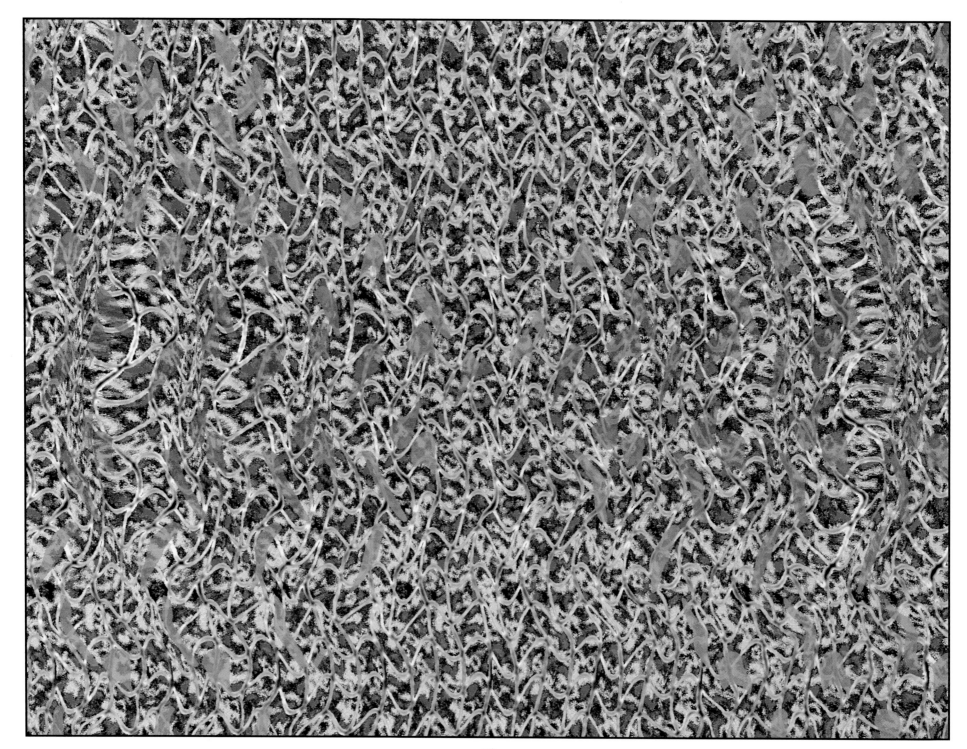

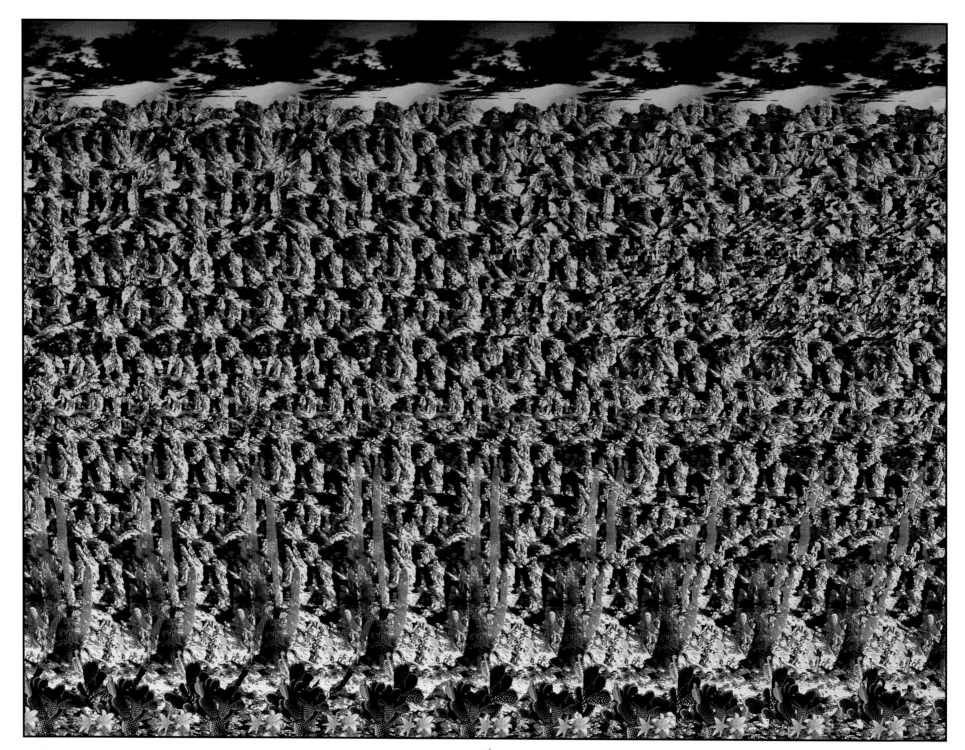

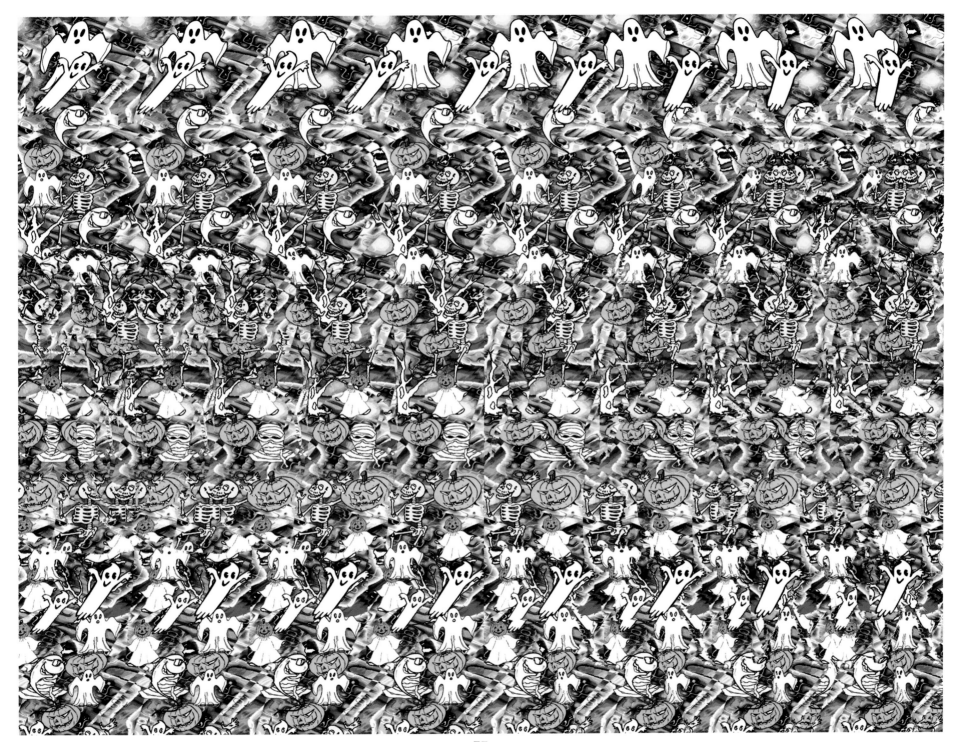

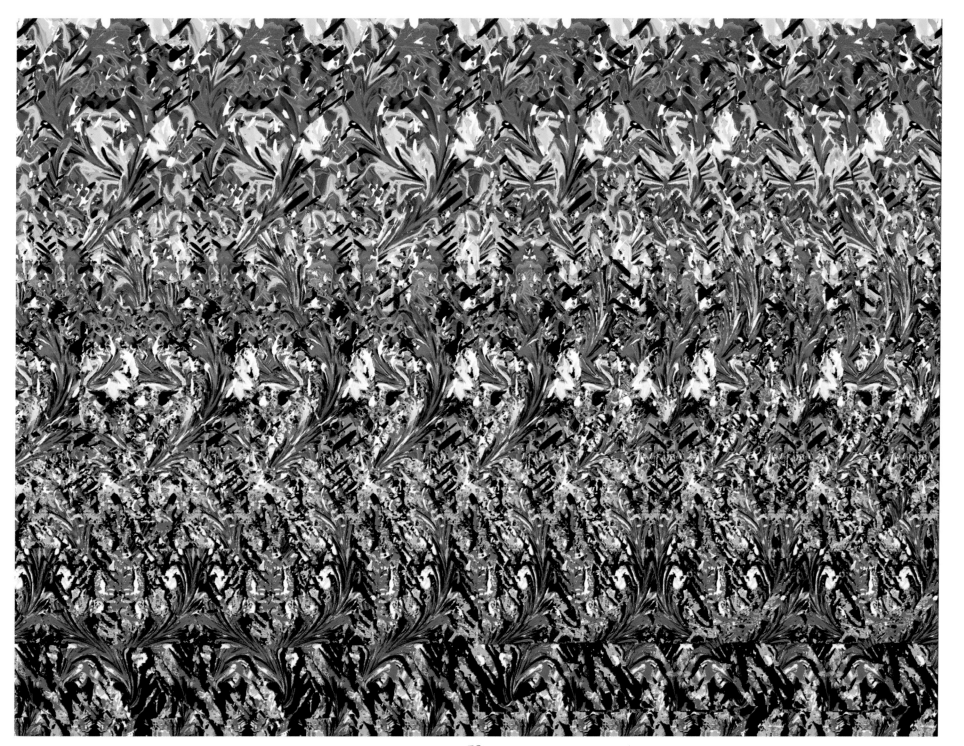

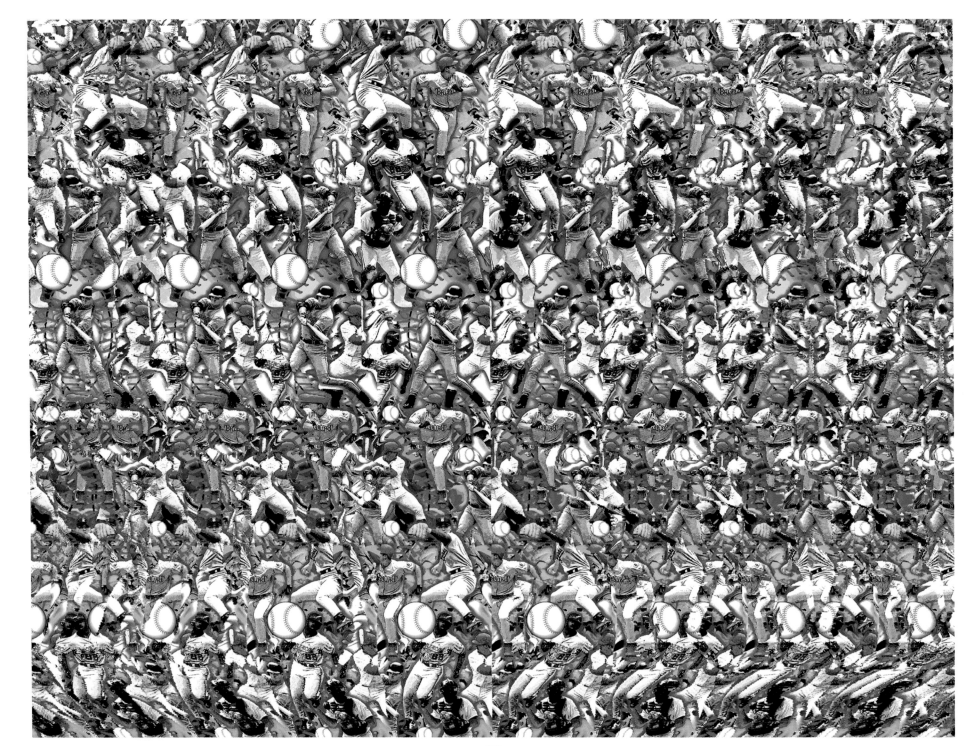

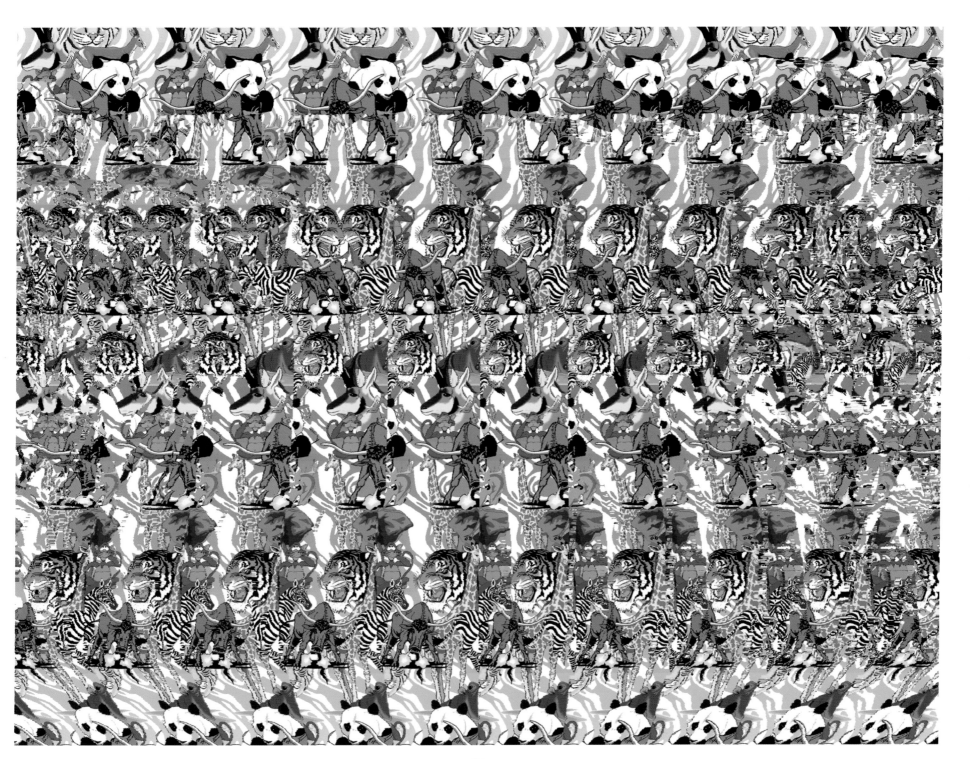

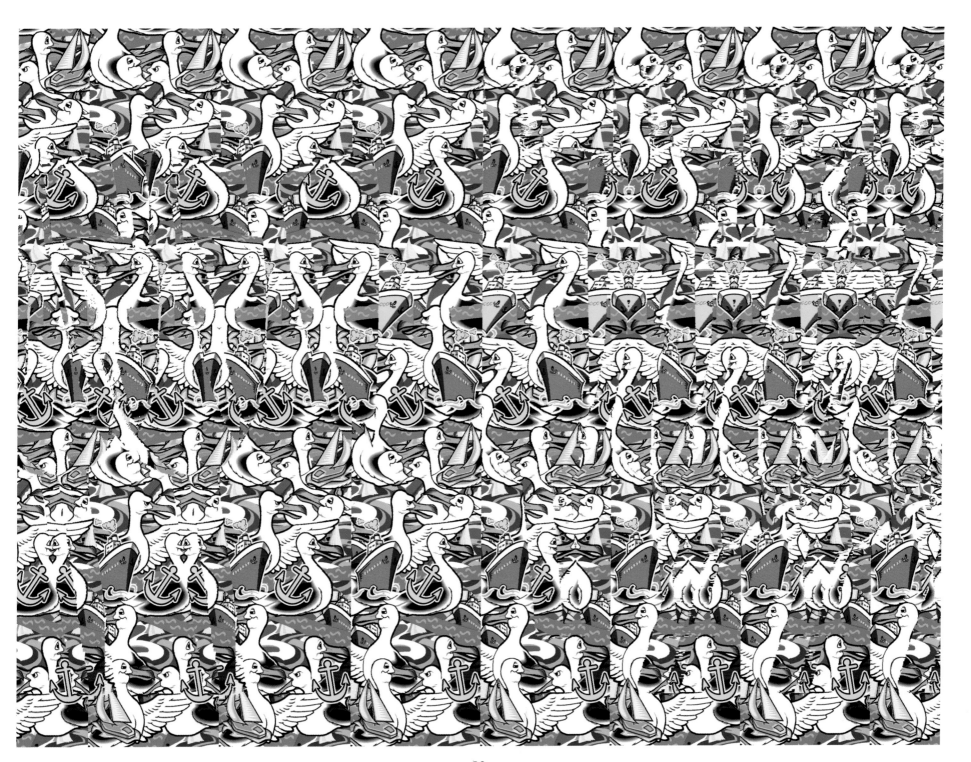

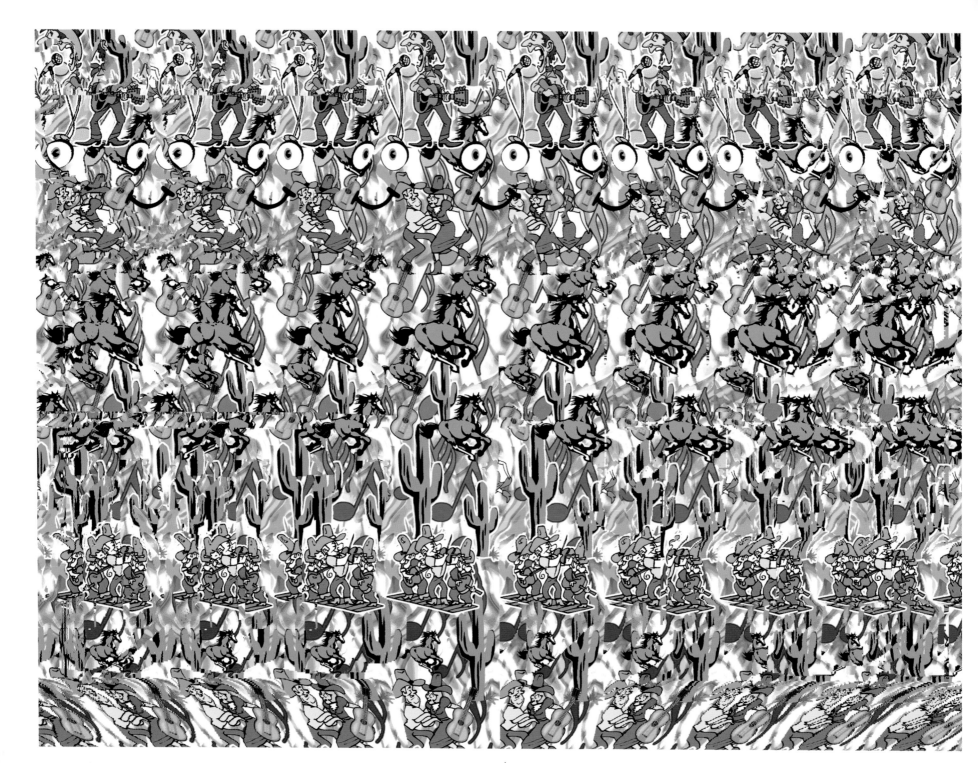

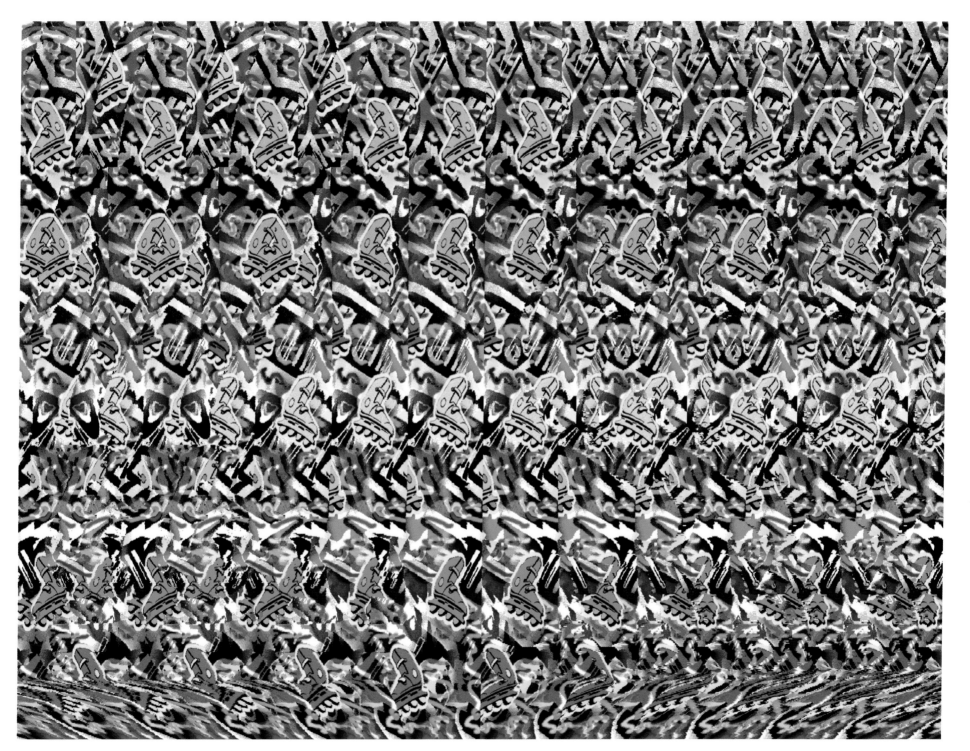

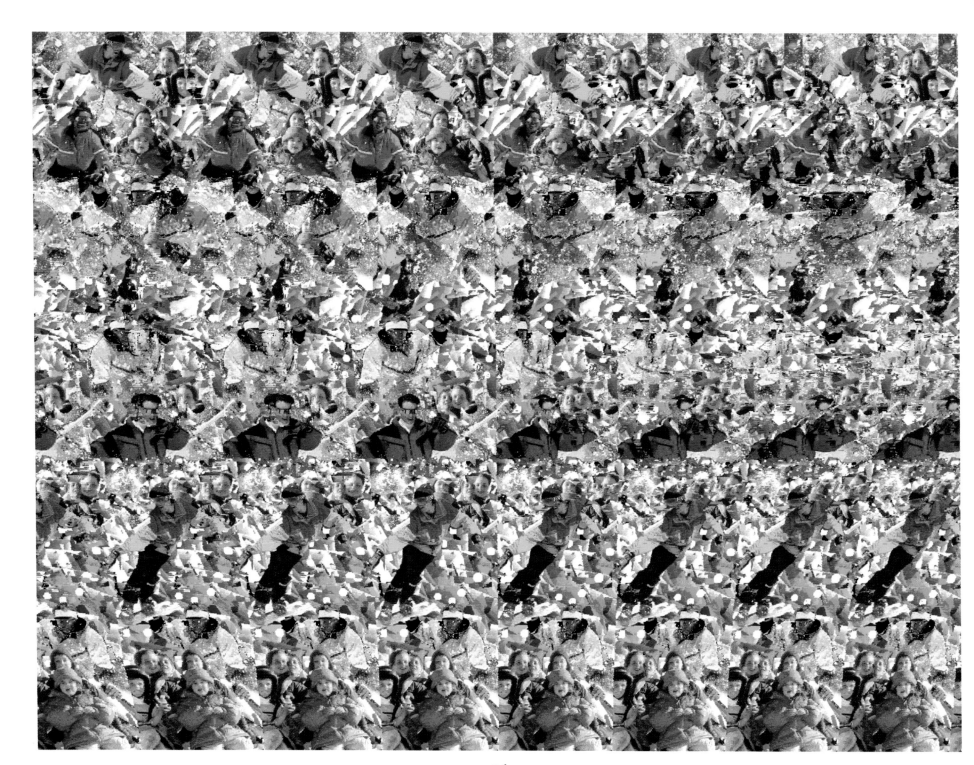

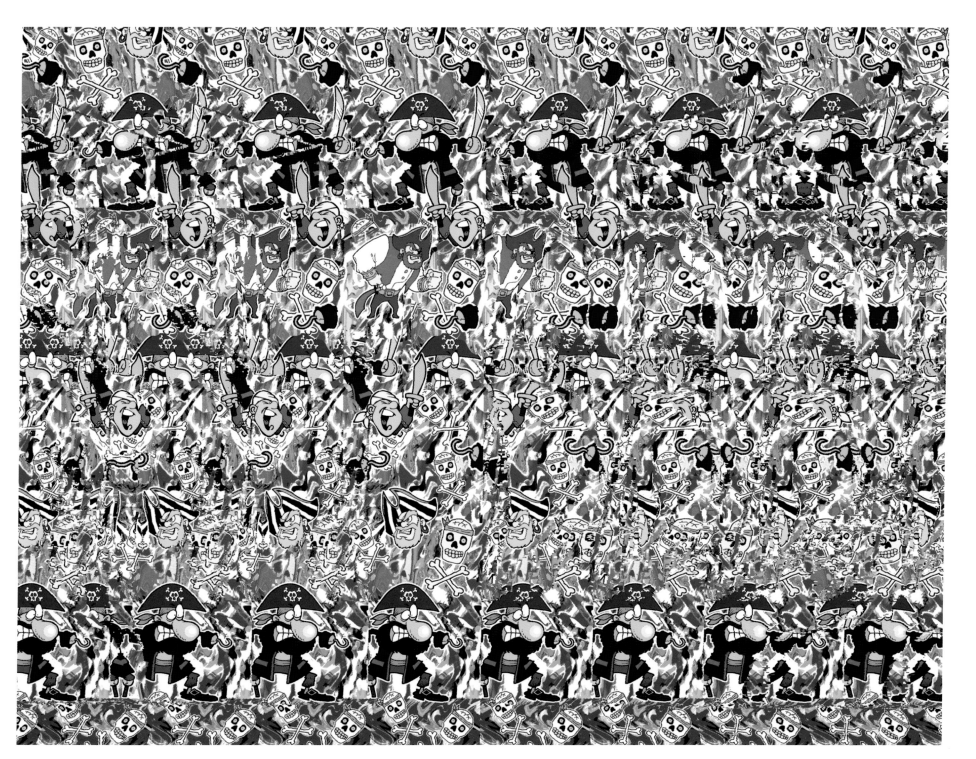

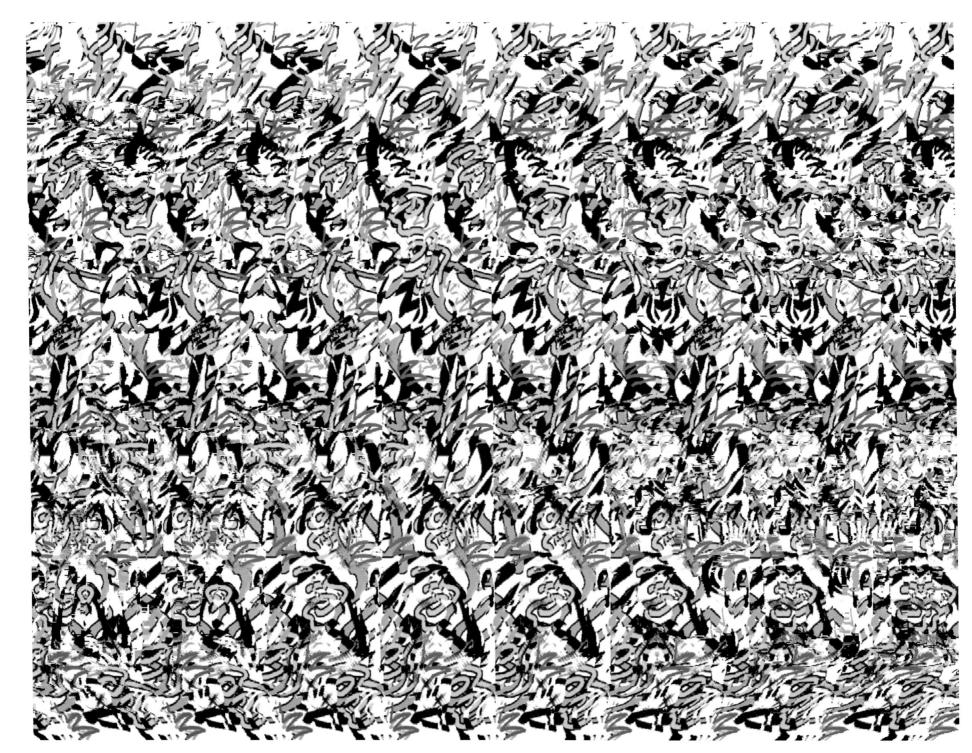

Pages 5-7 (No Images)
Page 8 Heart

Page 9 Star

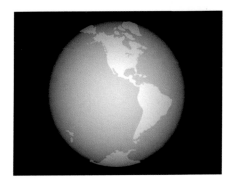

Page 10 The World

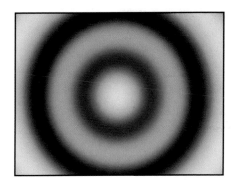

Page 11 Raindrop

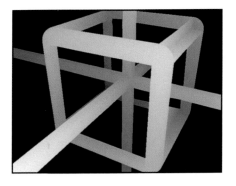

Page 12 Cube

Page 13 Boxing Kangaroos

Page 14 Train

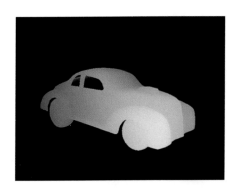

Page 15 Hot Rod

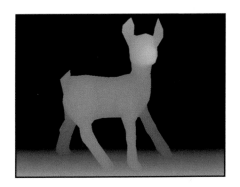

Page 16 Deer

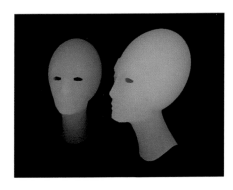

Page 17 Aliens

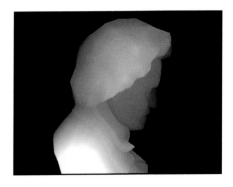

Page 18 Ludwig van Beethoven

Page 19 Lamb

Page 20 Paper Stars

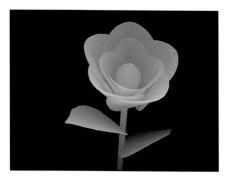

Page 21 Flower

Page 22 Still Life

Page 23 X29 / Fighter Plane

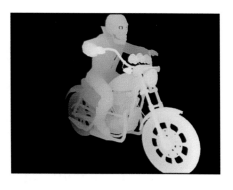

Page 24 Motor Bike

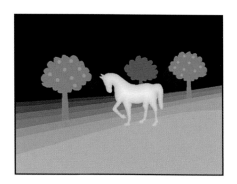

Page 25 Horse

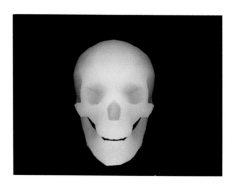

Page 26 Skull

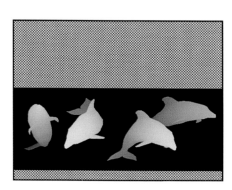

Page 27 Dolphins

Pages 28-29 Dinosaurs

Page 30 Crystal Ball

Page 31 Plain Cone

Page 32 Two-Layer Ball

Page 33 Buddha
Page 34 (No Image)

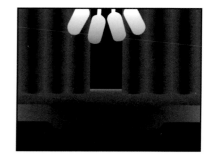

Page 35 Ballerinas

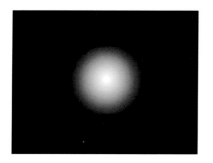

Page 36 Sphinx

Page 37 Lost Oasis

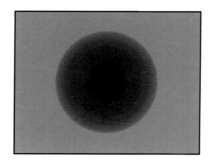

Page 38 Deer

Page 39 Storyland

Page 40 Dinner

Page 41 Baby Dinosaur

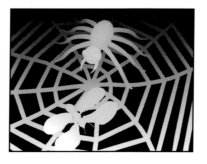

Page 42 Spider and Fly

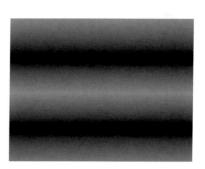

Page 43 Opt Art

Page 44 Andy's Bunny

Page 45 Zebras

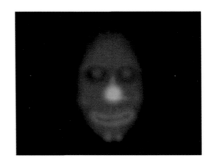

Page 46 Floater Clown

Page 47 Neon Clown

Page 48 Corner Kick

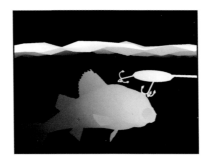

Page 49 Walleye

Pages 50-51 The Hunt

Page 52 Liberty

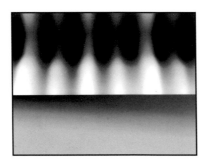

Page 53 Two-Layer, Three-Layer
Page 54 (No Image)

Page 55 The Eagle in Flight

Page 56 Tea Leaves

Front Watermark
(From Front Inside Cover)

Page 57 Chubby Rub

Page 58 Tom's Flower III

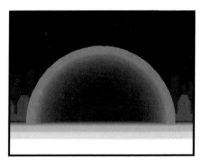

Page 59 Hatch Shell

Page 60 The Stretch

Page 61 Ruins
Page 62 (No Image)

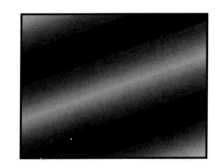

Page 63 Wild Thing

Page 64 Quick Draw

Page 65 RRREX

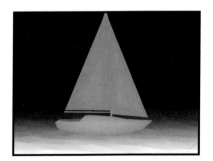

Page 66 Low Tide

Page 67 Visions

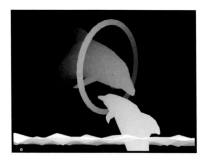

Page 68 Cool Tricks

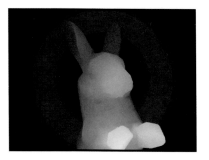

Page 69 Magic Hat

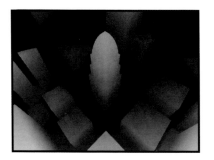

Page 70 Skyscraper of Stone
Page 71 (No Image)

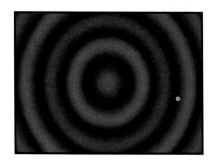

Page 72 3 Layer Water Drop
Page 73 (No Image)

Page 74 Grand Canyon

Page 75 Palm Springs
Pages 76 (No Image)

Pages 77 Boo

Page 78 Icarus Circus

Page 79 Cyclone

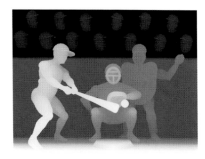

Page 80 Strike One

Page 81 Charge

Page 82 Two Layer 3-D

Page 83 Gulls & Buoys

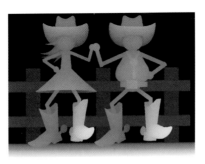

Page 84 Country Dancing

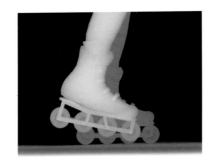

Page 85 In Line Skates

Page 86 Bunny Slope

Page 87 Shiver Me Timbers

Page 88 Ribbit

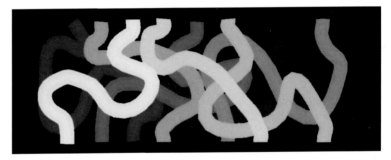

Back Watermark
(From Back Inside Cover)

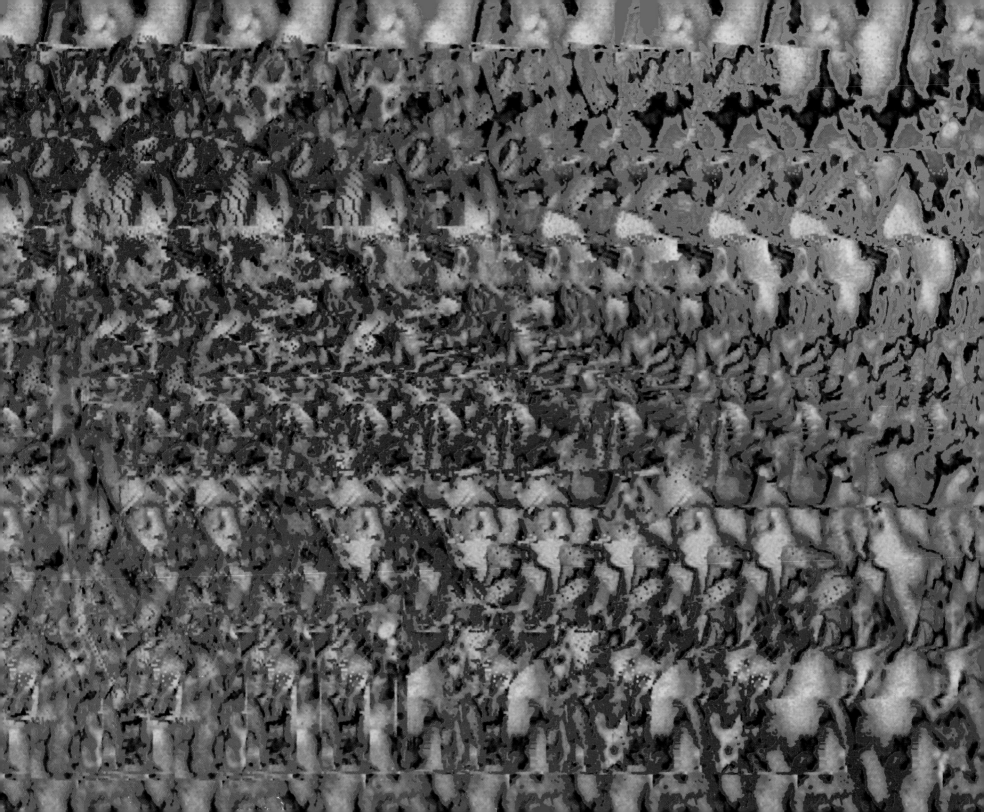